CALHOUN AND THE SOUTH CAROLINA NULLIFICATION MOVEMENT

BY

FREDERIC BANCROFT

———

BALTIMORE
THE JOHNS HOPKINS PRESS
1928

J. H. FURST CO., PRINTERS, BALTIMORE.

CONTENTS

CHAPTER I

CHAPTER II

CHAPTER III

CHAPTER VII

CHAPTER X

CALHOUN AND THE SOUTH CAROLINA NULLIFICATION MOVEMENT

CHAPTER I

TARIFF AND PROTECTION, 1816-28

The struggle that resulted in the Missouri Compromise was political in its purpose. For the protection of slavery in the distant future the South needed an open field for the increase of States with pro-slavery representation in Congress. The more clearly Southern leaders perceived this need, the more eager Northern leaders were to secure antislavery preponderance. The next critical sectional question—a combination of the tariff and nullification—was as thoroughly economic in origin as it was political and constitutional in its ultimate expression.

Temporary and exceptional influences of the period of the Napoleonic wars and of the War of 1812, which greatly lessened and at times virtually cut off foreign commerce, enormously stimulated the American manufacture of numerous kinds of articles that had previously been imported. Thus great and general public exigencies were met and skill and enterprise were developed in new directions. After the return of a not victorious peace

1

persons either especially patriotic or financially interested wished to preserve the new developments and otherwise to increase our national resources and fighting strength so as to render us less dependent on Europe. Calhoun, Lowndes and Henry Clay, having largely shaped the war-policy, not unnaturally agreed with the public men from regions most benefited by the new industries in desiring to shield them from the flood of cheap goods beginning to rush in from Europe.[1] Telfair of Georgia and John Randolph of Virginia were the most outspoken of the Southern free-traders that did not harbor such opinions.[2]

Lowndes, as chairman of the ways and means committee, reported the tariff bill of 1816. At a critical moment, April 4, 1816,[3] near the end of the debate, Calhoun was unexpectedly summoned from the room of the committee on national currency, of which he was chairman, and without preparation made what was probably the most

[1] Imports increased more than tenfold the first year and their value was about twice as much as in any year before the war. —Stanwood, 1 *American Tariff Controversies*, 131.

[2] *Annals of Congress*, 1815-16, pp. 1316-20, 1328-29.

[3] Without citing any authority, Crallé, the editor of *Calhoun's Works*, wrote (2 *Works*, 163) that Calhoun's speech was delivered Apr. 6, 1816, and that it was in reply to Tucker of Va., instead of to John Randolph. The *Annals of Congress*, 1815-16, pp. 1327-30, conclusively shows that the speech was on Apr. 4th and in reply to Randolph and others, Tucker's name not being even mentioned.

influential speech for the bill. Until then, the debate had been on the degree of protection to be afforded to our cotton and woollen manufactures, "all professing to be friendly to those infant establishments, and to be willing to extend to them adequate encouragement".[4] "Commerce and agriculture, till lately almost the only, still constitute the principal, sources of our wealth. * * * Neither agriculture, manufactures, nor commerce, taken separately, is the cause of wealth; it flows from the three combined, and can not exist without each. * * * When separated entirely and permanently they perish." War had separated them and ruined the country's finances. "When our manufactures are grown to a certain perfection, as they soon will [be] under the fostering care of [the] Government, we will [shall] no longer experience these evils. The farmer will find a ready market for his surplus produce; and, what is almost of equal consequence, a certain and cheap supply of all his wants. His prosperity will diffuse itself to every class in the community; and, instead of that languor of industry and individual distress now incident to a state of war and suspended commerce, the wealth and vigor of the community will not

---

[4] 2 *Calhoun's Works,* 163-73, and *Annals of Congress,* 1815-16, pp. 1329-36, give the speech in full.

be materially impaired. • • • To give perfection
to this state of things, it will be necessary to add,
as soon as possible, a system of internal improvements, and at least such an extension of our navy
as will prevent the cutting off our coasting trade.
• • • A prosperous commerce has poured an
immense amount of commercial capital into this
country. This capital has, till lately, found occu-
pation in commerce", but the conditions had
changed never to return. "What channel can it
take but that of manufactures? • • • Cotton
and woollen manufactures are • • • already
introduced to a great extent" • • •. Why, then,
did they need protection? "It is to put them
beyond the reach of contingency. • • • Should
the present owners be ruined, and the workmen
dispersed and turned to other pursuits, the country would sustain a great loss." Moreover, circumstances were most favorable to our attracting
much skill and industry from Europe, which
might be made "more valuable than the repeal of
the Edict of Nantz [Nantes] was to England".
Capital employed in manufacturing would excite
increased attention to internal improvements and
"bind together more closely our widely-spread
republic" and "form a new and most powerful
cement, and outweighing any political objections
that might be urged against the system. In his

opinion, the liberty and the union of this country were inseparably united." But should union be destroyed, liberty also would perish. There was, indeed, "a new and terrible danger, Disunion [undoubtedly referring to the Hartford convention and kindred movements]. This single word comprehended almost the sum of our political dangers; and against it we ought to be perpetually guarded." He evidently expected that the most essential manufactures would prosper after a temporary and moderate protective tariff and that agricultural as well as manufacturing and mining interests would be benefited by higher imposts and by extensive national aid to internal improvements.

The main support in passing the bill of 1816 came from the Middle States and the new States of Ohio, Kentucky and Tennessee—55 votes to 8. The South opposed it, 36 to 16, and New England favored it, 17 to 10. Even Calhoun and Lowndes could persuade only 2 of South Carolina's Representatives to stand with them, whereas 3 voted against the bill and 2 did not vote at all.[5] Daniel Webster, who opposed, and Lowndes and Calhoun, who championed, the bill did not truly represent their respective sections.

Benton said that before the War of 1812 the

---

[5] Meigs's figures are taken, 1 *Life of Calhoun*, 188-89.

object in levying the duties was to obtain revenue
and that the protection of manufactures was inci-
dental; now protection was the object and revenue
the incident, and to such a degree that a surplus
of $9,000,000 was collected. "No longer the 5 per
centum, the 10, 12½, 15, which formerly prevailed;
but all these doubled, with additions, and the introduction of minimum valuations, which gave to a
high duty the further advantage of being calculated on a fictitious value."[6] Yet it was, in general, only moderate protection. With certain
exceptions, the duty on woollen and on cotton
manufactures was to be 25 per cent. until 1819 and
thereafter it was to be 20. This promise to cautious protectionists was not kept. The average of
all the permanent tariff duties was so low—it was
about 20 per cent.[7]—or the tariff was so unscien-
tifically applied that many industries languished,
and the law brought more disappointment than
prosperity.[8]

There was at least one exception both as to the
degree and the failure of protection: it concerned
cotton manufactures and the fictitious valuations
of the vicious minimum system. The tariff law of
1816 provided that imported cotton goods costing

[6] Benton, 5 *Abridgment of Debates of Congress*, 645.

[7] Taussig, *Tariff History of the U. S.*, 18, 19, 68.

[8] 1 Stanwood, 155-56, 158.

less than 25 cents a yard should be deemed to have cost 25 cents a yard and should pay a duty of 25 per cent., that is 6¼ cents a yard. The use of power looms and the decline in the price of raw cotton reduced the cost of cotton goods. As this decreased, there was a relative increase in the actual percentage of the duty, which finally became so high as to be prohibitive, giving American manufacturers a virtual monopoly on coarse cottons. These unforeseen changes were the main causes of the early prosperity of the cotton factories.[9]

The advocates of protectionism as a basis for economic prosperity multiplied after the crisis of 1819. In 1820 they unsuccessfully tried to raise the customs duties, the Southern vote against it being 40 to 3, 12 not voting.[10] But they persisted and in 1824 were successful. The sole object in the minds of those who voted for the bill of that year was the protection of manufactures.[11] The average rate of duties was 37 per cent.,[12] nearly twice that of 1816. It was not a partisan, but a local, almost a personal, measure: in general, it was favored according to the demands of organizations interested in iron, wool, hemp, cot-

[9] Taussig, 29 ff., gives particulars.
[10] 1 Meigs, 324.　　　　[11] 1 Stanwood, 202.
[12] W. C. Ford, 3 *Lalor's Cyc. Political Science*, 861.

ton-bagging, whiskey or sugar, and its main support came from the Middle and the Western States. The planting South was almost unanimously against it,[13] having concluded from economic conditions and sectional disagreements that protectionism and slavery were antagonistic. New England was divided: Connecticut and Rhode Island were turning to manufacturing, but the most influential capital in the other States was still invested chiefly in enterprises associated with agriculture or maritime commerce. The duties on cotton and woollen goods were raised to 33⅓ per cent. from 25—where a law of April 20, 1818, had kept them, contrary to the promised reduction to 20 per cent. in 1819. This 33⅓ per cent. was of slight if any benefit to the manufacturers of woollens because the duty on wool was also increased from 15 to 30 per cent.[14]

The desire for protection always increases with its indulgence and the demands of the suppliants usually include greed as well as need. The West of that day—mainly Ohio, Indiana, Illinois, Kentucky and Missouri—wanted still more protection for wool, lead or hemp, and Louisiana more for sugar. And most of them desired extensive inter-

[13] Meigs says that " out of the 56 members of the House from the 7 contiguous States of Va., N. C., S. C., Ga., Ala., La. and Miss., but one single member voted Aye, while 54 voted Nay, and there was 1 not voting ".—1 *Calhoun*, 274.   [14] Taussig, 75.

nal improvements to facilitate the transportation
of their products to market. The prospective
beneficiaries were readily fascinated by Clay's
reasoning and his "American system". By this
time Massachusetts had the largest interest in the
woollen industry, but as yet many New England
capitalists were reluctant to embark in enterprises
dependent on legislation.

The Harrisburg convention, in the summer of
1827, was an elaborate enterprise led by allied
manufacturers in the Middle States to induce
Congress to put a high tariff on certain foreign
manufactured articles and on certain raw
materials. "It was the most energetic attempt
ever made to organize and give symmetry to the
protectionist movement." [15]

Manufacturers of cotton goods, having early
shown that they were masters of the art of pro-
moting self-interest through legislation, became
models for others with like purposes, especially
the manufacturers of woollens. These organized
in Boston in 1823, induced the legislature of Massachusetts to pass resolutions asking Congress to
give further protection to woollens, and Daniel
Webster—until a few years later an opponent of
protection—presented the resolutions in the
House. In 1827, a bill, giving the manufacturers

[15] W. G. Sumner, *Lectures on Protection in the U. S.*, 45.

all they requested and containing some of the worst features of the minimum system,[16] was defeated by the casting vote of Vice-President Calhoun, which laid it on the table. Van Buren had artfully arranged for a tie vote so as to compel Calhoun, his political rival, to lose popularity in Pennsylvania and New York, if he opposed the bill, and to arouse hostility in the South, if he favored it.

The tariff bill of 1828 was the product of those years of agitation and organization. To win assistance, the scope of protection was much widened. Anti-protectionists unwisely and in vain conspired to defeat this bill by favoring an increase in the cost of the raw materials used by otherwise favored manufacturers, hoping that this would cause these manufacturers to oppose the bill. The plot failed. This "tariff of abominations", this "economic monstrosity", was enacted in May, 1828. "It was the work of politicians and manufacturers", said Benton; and with naïve frankness he proceeded to supply thoroughly convincing evidence of it by telling what he had done. "My personal position was that of a great many others in the three protective sections—opposed to the policy, but going with it, on account of the interest of the State in the protec-

16 Taussig, 41-42, 80-82.

tion of some of its productions. I moved an additional duty on lead, equal to one hundred per centum, and it was carried."[17] "It might be thought high; but he could say that it was not too high for the benefit of Missouri and Illinois; and if rejected, there would be nothing in the bill to induce him to vote for it." And Senator Rowan of Kentucky—although opposed to the tariff (except when for revenue) because it impoverished one class of laborers for the purpose of enriching another, and believing that it was paid by the consumer—said that as the organ of Kentucky he felt bound to surrender his individual opinion and favor that of his State.[18] As if hemp and whiskey were sovereign in Kentucky and lead were sovereign in Missouri or Illinois!

According to Professor Sumner,[19] "The industrial interests of twelve millions of people had been thrown into an arena where there was little knowledge of economic principles, and no information about the industrial state of the country, or about the special industries. It being assumed that the legislature could, would, and was about to, confer favors and advantages, there was a scramble to see who should get the most." The

[17] Benton, 1 *Thirty Years' View*, 95, 97.
[18] Benton, 9 *Abridgment of Debates*, 591-92.
[19] *Andrew Jackson*, 205.

woollen manufacturers hoped to obtain the lion's share by having the vicious mimimum system made more vicious. The duty "on woollens was 40 per cent for a year, then 45 per cent, there being four minima, 50 cents, $1.00, $2.50, $4.00. All which cost over $4.00 were to be taxed 45 per cent for a year, then 50 per cent." The manufacturers had planned to have all woollens costing between 51 cents and $2.50 per square yard (both inclusive) taxed as if they cost $2.50. This would have put a duty of $1.00 on them, which would have made a tax of nearly 200 per cent. on the woollens that cost only a little above 50 cents per square yard. But the opposition inserted a $1.00 minimum, which greatly lessened the plunder and accordingly enraged the woollen men.[20]

Increased duties on certain raw materials prevented the increased duties on some manufactured articles from being of much, if any, benefit to the American manufacturers. Such was especially the case with the New England shipbuilders. "The prohibitory duties on the coarse cottons and woollens with which the slaves were clothed, on sugar, salt, and iron manufactures, gave the planters no choice but to buy of domestic producers at prices averaging 40 per cent. higher than in foreign markets."[21]

[20] Sumner, *Jackson*, 205.
[21] Coman, *Industrial History of the U. S.*, 196.

These efforts to obtain special favors have been likened to a "mere game of snatch". And the frank declarations of Members of Congress that they voted according to the interests of constituents, instead of according to their own intelligent convictions as to national welfare, disclose a burlesque of statesmanship, which unfortunately has not yet become a lost art.

CHAPTER II

SOUTH CAROLINA'S OPPOSITION AND ECONOMIC CONDITION

A high authority has said that the first suggestion in Congressional debates that the tariff for protection was unconstitutional was made in 1816 by a Southern member, but that Daniel Webster, in a speech in Faneuil Hall, October 20, 1820, was the first to elaborate the idea. Clay was not far wrong in believing that the constitutional question was not raised before 1820 or 1822. "It was first hinted, then controverted, and soon after expanded into nullification." [1] As early as 1820, during the excitement about Missouri, the South Carolina house of representatives opposed protection, but it was also opposed to arraying the States as distinct and independent sovereignties against the General Government.[2] This showed that the most advanced thinkers were already contemplating the use of state sovereignty for defense. Again, in December, 1824, after the enactment of the protective tariff of that year, the senate of South Carolina passed resolutions, drafted by Calhoun's antagonist, William Smith,

[1] 1 Stanwood, 293-94.

[2] Ames, *State Documents on Federal Relations*, 135.

14

denouncing as unconstitutional both the protective tariff and internal improvements, but the house tabled them and otherwise showed its unwillingness to question the constitutionality of acts of Congress.[3] This was after Senator Hayne and other South Carolinians in Congress had opposed the tariff bill of 1824 by denying its constitutionality.

By December, 1825, sentiment in South Carolina had changed so rapidly that resolutions similar to those previously rejected were passed by both houses. This was the first official condemnation by any State legislature of the internal improvement and the tariff acts.[4] For some time the opposition was mainly journalistic, oratorical and unorganized, many persons merely refusing to buy articles whose prices were supposed to be augmented by the tariff. Then came protesting resolutions—inspired by ambitious and fiery politicians and loudly applauded at motley gatherings in cities, villages and at courthouses—designed to be sent to Columbia and to Washington.

The Harrisburg convention was oil poured on the fire. In December, 1827, the South Carolina

[3] Ames, *State Documents* etc., 138, 138. Prof. Ames has advised the present writer that the resolutions cited p. 138 and referred to (p. 136) as adopted were only reported by a committee to the South Carolina house of representatives.

[4] Ames, 136, 139-40.

legislature resolved that the Constitution was a compact between independent sovereignties; that in case of any violation of that compact by Congress it was the right not only of the people but of the legislatures to remonstrate; and it instructed South Carolina's Senators and requested her Representatives to oppose every increase of the tariff to protect domestic manufactures and all appropriations for internal improvements or in favor of the American Colonization Society, because such measures would be beyond the constitutional power of Congress.[5] Nevertheless the tariff of 1828 was promptly enacted.

Popular resentment against protectionism had grown rapidly. Duties on woollens had increased the cost of every blanket and of every winter suit bought for slaves, and the tariff on hemp was a tax on common ropes and on the cover of every bale of cotton.[6] Such facts, embellished by fancy and oratory, made the North appear very prosperous as a result of an alleged sectional conspiracy to tax the South, while the South seemed doomed to wretchedness. Opinions were mani-

[5] For the text see Ames, 144-45.

[6] "Why," exclaimed James Hamilton, Jr., in the House of Representatives as early as Feb., 1824, "for the benefit of Ky., we are to be taxed, in round numbers, sixty thousand dollars a year in the small State which I represent"—Annals of Congress 1823-24, p. 1518.

fested by refusals to buy what was produced in protectionist States and by the conspicuous wearing of homespun. South Carolina's Representatives in Washington, dressed in it, were reported to be making a strange contrast with those "who walked abroad in all the pride of Saxon broadcloth".[7] A certain judge, refused to eat Irish potatoes because they came from the North. A prominent lawyer said he would walk his circuit rather than use horses from Kentucky.[8]

There had been only less intemperate indignation in other Southern States. By a great majority in each branch the legislature of Virginia in 1826 and again in 1827 resolved that protectionism was unconstitutional. Even the tariff law of 1824 was called "unwise, unjust, unequal and oppressive". Georgia's protest contained this gentle but well-directed sarcasm: "While manufacturing companies and self-created delegates, pretending to represent whole States, assemble for the purpose of directing the Congress what measures they must adopt, surely the legislature of a State, without much violence to any known rule of modesty, may respectfully offer a counter-remonstrance to such a growing temper of dictation." The legislature of North Carolina said that pro-

---

[7] Charleston *Courier*, Dec. 15, 1828.

[8] Perry, 2 *Reminiscences*, 205.

tectionism "palsies every effort of the agricultur-
ist, withers the product of his industry, and greatly
impairs foreign commerce". The legislature of
Alabama referred to the Harrisburg convention
as representing "the allied powers of avarice, monopoly and ambition" and alleged that there was
an "endeavor to throw the overgrown weight of
the General Government upon the Southern and
Southwestern States, dry up their commerce by
sapping its foundation, degrade them from the
proved equality of the Compact, into the humiliat-
ing condition of dependent tributaries to the
greedy monopolists of the North and East." [9]

This widespread agreement with South Carolina in regard to the unconstitutionality and
injuriousness of protectionism did not satisfy her.
With marked exceptions, from 1789 to 1824
South Carolinians in Congress had opposed the
protective tariff on account of its inexpediency
and injustice, not its unconstitutionality. [10] Until
the Harrisburg convention of 1827 made the tariff
question poignant, the South had put more stress
on objections to internal improvements than on
protectionism. [11] To no other State, at that time,

[9] Ames, 140-44, 146, 149, 150.

[10] David F. Houston, *A Study of Nullification in South Carolina*,
3-4. This is a monograph of rare scholarship, independence and
lucidity.

[11] Ames, 133, 134, 136, 140, 142, 143.

was slavery so vital as to South Carolina: in no old State was it either so profitable or would its abolition so violently have changed the whole social and economic organization. And South Carolinians were the more ready to believe that the tariff was unconstitutional because they were still much perturbed by very recent antislavery manifestations, such as the struggle of 1819-21 about barring slavery from Missouri and north of 36° 30', the threatened Vesey insurrection in South Carolina in 1822, the rapid growth and antislavery trend of the Colonization Society, and the propositions in Congress and nine Northern State legislatures for compensated emancipation and colonization, for which the favorite plan was to use the public lands as a source of revenue.[12] South Carolinians, soon to be leaders in nullification, repeatedly showed that their greatest fear was that a centralized Federal Government with surplus revenue might adopt some such scheme;

[12] Meigs of New York made such a proposition in the House in 1820.—Benton, 6 *Abridgment of Debates*, 502. In 1824 the Ohio legislature proposed gradual and compensated emancipation and colonization by the aid of the U. S. treasury, and eight other States soon endorsed the plan.—Ames, *State Documents* etc., 203 ff., gives the text and many details. Rufus King introduced similar resolutions in the U. S. Senate in 1825.—*Cong. Deb.*, 1824-25, 623. That some of these propositions were chiefly for personal or partisan purposes did not make them less significant and irritating.

and the legislatures of Georgia, South Carolina, Missouri, Mississippi, Louisiana and Alabama emphatically expressed their disapproval of anything of that character.[13] Without these various political or social kindlings protectionism would undoubtedly have aroused persistent opposition in South Carolina, but it would not have been one-half so excited. The North was believed to have taken the aggressive for sectional interests, and it was only natural that it should be met accordingly: sectionalism almost compels sectionalism. And because the protective tariff increased the prices of nearly all manufactured articles the Southerners bought and gave them no appreciable compensation, it was well suited to be used as an immediate and general irritant, whereas questions of internal improvements, centralization and colonization were more remote and did not appeal to all persons.

By comparing South Carolina with other States, especially Northern or Western, it was easy for South Carolinians to fancy that their State was in a positive decline. More or less distinct evidences of great lack of prosperity were apparent on all hands. Now we know the main causes. Then they were little better than mat-

[13] Ames, 203.

ters of conjecture, for the significant facts were still largely unrecorded or not comprehended. The abolition of primogeniture in 1791 had brought about the division of estates of decedents and accordingly lessened the incomes of previously favored persons. During the three decades, 1800-30, the average increase of South Carolina's white population was only nine, ten and eight per cent., respectively—about one-fourth the percentage of the average increase of the white population in the whole United States for that period. The percentage of increase in her slave population during these three decades was 34, 31 and 22 per cent.—about three times that of the white population. There may well have been a premonition that in the next decade the decline would be still greater; in fact, between 1830-40, the white population increased less than one-half of one per cent. and the slave population but little more than three and one-half per cent.[14]

Much more noticeable in Charleston was the 50 per cent. decrease of imports into South Carolina during the six years 1823-28—from $2,419,101 to $1,242,048 by a continuous decline of from about $25,000 to more than $350,000 annually.[15]

[14] *Preliminary Rept., Eighth Census* (1860), 124-129, gives the precise figures.

[15] 2 Meigs, 42-44, gives fuller statistics and the authorities.

These and other declines, known or surmised, were rumored and excitedly discussed until an explanation was demanded. It was easy to convince South Carolinians that the tariff was a tax, for such it was indirectly; and they exhibited, in an exaggerated degree, only a common trait when they assumed that a conspicuous tax was the cause of their misfortunes.

In 1825 McDuffie, when still a nationalist, rightly attributed the unfavorable condition of the old States of the South largely to the cheap public lands in the West.[16]   Three years later, James Hamilton, Jr., eager to arouse his constituents, made these oratorical assertions: as a result of protection, so many South Carolinians had been sent on their sorrowful pilgrimage to the West that Carolina's days were numbered and her pros-

[16] " In no part of Europe will you see the same indications of decay [as in the South]. Deserted villages—houses falling into ruins—impoverished lands thrown out of cultivation. Sir, I believe that if the public lands had never been sold, the aggregate amount of the national wealth would have been greater at this moment. * * * But, while the Government continues, as it now does, to give them away, they will draw the population of the older States, and still farther increase the effect which is already distressingly felt, and which must go to diminish the value of all those States possess. * * * At this moment we are selling to the people of the West, lands at one dollar and twenty-five cents an acre, which are fairly worth fifteen, and which would sell at that price if the markets were not glutted."—*Cong. Debates*, 1824-25, 254.

perity gone; the fox was sleeping in security and peace on the very hearthstones where hospitality had once kindled the most genial fires, and the owl was sending forth to a listening solitude her melancholy descant to mark the spot where the tariff had caused desolation.[17] The protective tariff was, indeed, injurious and intensely exasperating; but it could not have been the main cause of desolation, for much of this existed before either of the high tariffs was enacted. As McDuffie indicated, it was the extensive movement of population with youthful energy, slaves and other capital to cheap, fertile, new lands in the Southwest, and the consequent over-production of cotton, that were the chief factors of South Carolina's economic misfortunes. And it was generally known to persons of intelligence.[18]

[17] Speech of Oct. 21, 1828, p. 12.

[18] Madison, 4 *Writings* (Cong. ed.), 261, is clear and concise about these influences. Calhoun wrote May 4, 1828: "Never was there such universal and severe pressure on the whole South, excepting the portion which plants sugar. Our staples hardly return the expense of cultivation, and land and negroes have fallen to the lowest price, and can scarcely be sold at the present depressed rates." He considered the tariff as "one of the great instruments of our impoverishment; and if persisted in must reduce us to poverty, or compel us to an entire change of industry." July 10, 1828: "There is almost universal embarrassment among the people of the staple States, which they almost unanimously attribute to the high duties."—*Calhoun Correspondence*, 264-66.

Legaré said July 4, 1831: "It is owing to this policy [of

But how could such fundamental influences be almost ignored? The leisure or semi-leisure class in South Carolina was relatively much larger than in any other State. Politics was their chief common interest, the source of greatest public entertainment and mental activity, and exciting

protection] that the Government has to bear the blame of whatever evils befall the people from natural or accidental causes—that whether our misfortunes spring from the barrenness of the earth, or the inclemency of the seasons, or the revolutions of commerce, or a defective system of domestic and rural economy—or, in short, from any other source, they are all indiscriminately imputed to the tariff. The decay and desolation which are invading many parts of the lower country—the fall in the price of our great staple commodity—the comparative unproductiveness of slave labor—are confidently declared to be the effects of this odious and tyrannical monopoly. Sir, firmly convinced as I am that there is no sort of connection (or an exceedingly slight one) between these unquestionable facts and the operation of the tariff law, yet I do not wonder at the indignation which the imposition of such a burthen of taxation has excited in our people in the present unprosperous state of their affairs."— Legaré, 1 *Writings*, 272.

" Our fields are deserted, and the labor that tilled them has fled to Ala., La. and elsewhere! Our cities are falling into ruins —our commerce gone—and our mechanics without employment. We have been in the habit of placing everything to the account of the accursed tariff, * * * yet much more might be safely put down to the account of the continued withdrawal from the State of the capital accumulated by mercantile operations, to foreign countries."—J. L. Wilson, *Speeches in S. C. Conv. of March, 1833*, 30.

Houston, *Nullification in S. C.*, 44, shows that the overproduction of cotton was perhaps the greatest direct cause of hard times.

harangues were most effective. When the decla-
mation could not be heard and the showy action
seen, imaginative readers were easily influenced
by the ardent rhetoric of printed speeches, public
letters and editorial articles. And the display of
such talents was the surest means of attaining distinction. Things were indeed going very ill with
South Carolina. Moreover, highly colored traditions of riches and luxuries prior to the abolition of primogeniture made a sad contrast with
the actual conditions a third of a century later,
when resources were scattered and opportunities
for money-making were few. Yet these things did
not at all lessen the belief of South Carolinians in
their own superiority or in that of slavery. And
now that it was feared that the Constitution might
not long protect slavery, nerves were so much on
edge that dire threats were common as to what
would be done if it should be touched. Such persons in such circumstances lack thrift and good
judgment, have no taste for serious study, and
self-criticism is foreign to their natures. Accordingly, idle, discontented and ambitious men,
especially young men, were easily persuaded that
it was time to assert their rights, to do something
positive, radical, heroic—something that would
turn things back toward old conditions or hasten
them forward toward a realization of cherished

dreams. For years the orators, pamphleteers and journalists were far ahead of the people, but with confidence and increasing determination they held to their chosen task.[19]

[19] Boucher's thoroughgoing study, *The Nullification Controversy in South Carolina,* 23 ff., 55 ff., 83 ff., gives many details.

CHAPTER III

EARLY LEADERS IN NULLIFICATION

Judge William Smith—whom a distinguished contemporary called "the wisest and most consistent statesman South Carolina ever produced in my day and time"[1]—seems to have been most influential in starting the South Carolina reaction against centralization. He became United States Senator in 1817 and soon began a vigorous attack on the protective tariff and internal improvements, representing Calhoun as their great exponent. Later, when the assertion of so-called state-rights went beyond protests and constitutional methods, he halted. Smith's hostility to Calhoun and Calhoun's reciprocation of it led to Smith's defeat by Robert Y. Hayne, a ready, prepossessing leader among radicals unafraid of any extreme; but Smith soon became Hayne's colleague by appointment to fill out another's unexpired term.

James Hamilton, Jr., once a stanch nationalist, joined the anti-nationalists and rose to the highest rank by virtue of audacity, eloquence and abilities as leader and manager. He suggested the nullification clubs—"Jacobin" clubs, as the

[1] Benj. F. Perry, 1 *Reminiscences*, 81.

27

Unionists dubbed them—which were established in every county, held meetings every month on sale day, created tireless agitators and soon transformed opinions into actions.[2]

Among those in the legislature who were most violent against the tariff was a young man soon to become attorney-general and a few years longer to bear the name of Robert Barnwell Smith. This was the elder Robert Barnwell Rhett of later fame.

Probably the man that directly made the most converts to nullification was Robert J. Turnbull with his *Crisis*.[3] Turnbull ardently maintained that there was a permanent conflict of economic interests between the South and the North and West, and that the growing nationalism in the government was unconstitutional and would turn against slavery.[4] He violently opposed everything suggesting nationalism or consolidation— especially colonization, for he expected that colonization would be the line of attack in the attempt to abolish slavery, the apple of the Southern eye. South Carolinians solemnly

[2] Perry, 1 *Reminiscences*, 143; 2 *Reminiscences*, 209-10.

[3] *The Crisis or Essays on the Usurpations of the Federal Government*, by Brutus, was a series of letters beginning in the Charleston *Mercury* early in 1827 and soon collected in a small volume.

[4] *Crisis*, 7-15, 26, 89, 109-10.

likened the *Crisis* to the *Federalist,* but dissimi-
larities were more conspicuous. The aim of Alexander Hamilton, Madison and Jay in the *Federalist* was to make the Constitution seem large and
comprehensive enough to suit the needs of the
whole country. With great ingenuity Turnbull
undertook to prove that the Constitution was
really no more national than the special needs of
South Carolina. Where the *Federalist* was stu-
diously philosophical and rational, to convince the
mind, the *Crisis*—"the first bugle call in the
South to rally", as James Hamilton, Jr., said—
was heated and dogmatic, to excite passion and to
prompt to action. Yet the immediate success of
the *Federalist* in its extensive field was less nearly
complete than was that of the *Crisis* in South
Carolina. Turnbull's qualities suited the cause to
which he devoted them. By frequent and usually
intemperate speeches, articles and public letters
he easily held his leadership, for the people
accepted his avowal that he sought nothing for
himself and that his doctrines all came from Jefferson,[5] who had recently died, and his name was

---

[5] *Speeches in March, 1833, Convention,* 52. "My principles
have not only been incorporated in the resolutions, remonstrances
and protests of our own legislature, but they have been adopted
by other Southern legislatures. * * * And whence are these
doctrines? * * * Is it to the author of Brutus that you would
ascribe the praise? * * * He has trodden no path which has

one to conjure with. Except in their violent extremes and impetuous flow, there was little in Turnbull's ideas that had not previously been expressed by Charles Pinckney, Judge Smith, Hayne or Dr. Cooper; but to the unsophisticated public his angry and forceful assertions seemed fresh and unanswerable. Dying before the excitement subsided, the radicals erected a monument to his memory, called him their prophet, and Hamilton in his eulogy said: "No soldier ever marched to the Holy Land with a higher burst of enthusiasm." Indeed, Turnbull did most to make the nullification campaign a "burst of enthusiasm".

Dr. Thomas Cooper, president of South Carolina College, 1820-33, was sometimes called the father of nullification in South Carolina. He was at least one of those that did most to help precipitate it. His intensely anti-national pamphlet *Consolidation,* published in 1824, classed Calhoun and McDuffie with John Quincy Adams and General Jackson as extreme centralizationists. According to Jefferson, all enlightened acquaintances of Cooper regarded him as "the greatest man in America in the powers of his mind and in acquired information". John Quincy Adams

not been hallowed by the footsteps of Jefferson."—Turnbull's speech, *Proceedings of the State-Rights Celebration at Charleston, July 1, 1830,* pp. 37-38.

characterized him as "a learned, ingenious, scientific and talented madcap".[6] Both were right. Cooper's stormy, checkered career in Europe as well as in the United States, his intellectual independence, originality, varied learning, his great quantity of work as writer and editor and his skill in controversy—these gave prestige and a romantic background to his academic distinctions.[7] In his *Political Economy*, published in

[6] Houston, *Nullification*, 56.

[7] Born in London in 1759, educated at Oxford, he was admitted to the bar and practised law a few years. He early championed democracy in England, then the Girondists in France and dared publicly to challenge the opinions of even Edmund Burke. He visited the United States in 1793, settled in Penn. in 1794 and was soon practising law. Before long he was violently attacking the Administration of John Adams, for which he was condemned, under the sedition act, and served six months in prison and paid a fine of $400,—which he, to the end of his life, protested against and demanded back and which ten years after his death Congress repaid his heirs with interest.—C. F. Himes, *Life and Times of Thomas Cooper*, 70. In turn, he was a land commissioner in Penn., a judge, a professor of chemistry in Dickinson College and then in Penn. University. When Thomas Jefferson was organizing the University of Va. he had Cooper made professor of chemistry, mineralogy and natural philosophy and, later, law and expected him to be "the cornerstone of our ediface" (Himes, 37-38); but before long he was compelled to resign on account of his free-thinking. He was then called to a professorship in S. C. College and soon became its president. Less rapidly, but with the same result, a similar storm gathered in Columbia: he was forced out of the presidency and soon withdrew from the College. His remaining years were successfully spent in editing the *Statutes of S. C.*, in which work he showed great ability and learning. Malone's *Cooper* is vivid and interesting.

1826, he was a militant disciple of Adam Smith.
In fact, he was militant in all things. At an anti-
tariff meeting at Columbia in the summer of 1827
he had said with inflammatory eloquence: ''There
is not a petty manufacturer in the Union, from the
owner of a spinning factory, to the maker of a
hobnail,—from the mountains of Vermont to the
swamps of the Patapsco, who is not pressing forward to the plunder; and who may not be expected
to worry Congress with petitions, memorials and
querulous statements for permission to put his
hands   into   the   planter's   pocket. • • • The
avowed object now is, by means of a drilled and
managed majority in Congress, permanently to
force upon us a system, whose effect will be to sacrifice the South to the North, by converting us into
colonies and tributaries—to tax *us* for their own
emolument—to claim the right of disposing of our
honest earnings—to forbid us to buy from our
most valuable customers—to irritate into retalia-
tion our foreign purchasers, and thus confine our
raw material to the home market—in short, to
impoverish the planter and to stretch the purse of
the manufacturer.'' [8] To the ears of this impet-

[8] 33 *Niles's Register*, 28. Such extreme beliefs were naturally
accompanied with suspicions of personal corruption: '' Among the
instances of self-deception, I can easily believe that a rumored
investment of $50,000 in the Lowell manufacture, may have
conquered the heterodoxy of Mr. Webster's former opinions, and

uous free-thinker the words *American system*—
"this system of fraud, robbery and usurpation"—
sounded like a base libel on the American character. For a climax he suggested that the South
would "ere long be compelled to calculate the
value of our Union"—a Union in which "the
South has always been the loser and the North
always the gainer * * * , where the North
demand to be our masters and we are required to
be their tributaries".

The enactment of "the tariff of abominations"
was sure to increase discontent and the influence
of the radicals. The South Carolina delegation in
Congress, except Senator William Smith, immediately met at Senator Hayne's lodgings to consider a course of action. James Hamilton, Jr.,
said that, because his constituents had been
insulted and their interests trampled upon, he had
resolved to withdraw from Congress and not
return unless specially instructed to do so. But
some of his colleagues dissuaded him from taking
such precipitate action; and all soon agreed to
defer decision until they could hasten home, learn
the status of public opinion in their districts and
further exchange views.[9]

brought him over to the true faith: similar reasons may have
operated as inducements to other learned gentlemen to abandon
their heresies."

[9] 35 *Niles's*, 202.

CHAPTER IV

CALHOUN AND THE "SOUTH CAROLINA EXPOSITION".—GEORGE MCDUFFIE

Since March, 1825, Calhoun had been Vice-President and John Quincy Adams President. Previously Calhoun was Monroe's Secretary of War for more than seven years. He was in no way responsible for either the tariff of 1824 or that of 1828. During the struggle over Missouri and for several years after he became, early in 1822, an open aspirant for the Presidency his attitude toward public questions appeared to be that of a liberal-minded nationalist. His meticulous yet fair and scholarly biographer, Mr. Meigs, has found many reasons to believe that a gradual change began early in the 'twenties, but the public knew nothing of it until much later. What was known, as Mr. Meigs also shows, was that Calhoun's friends in Pennsylvania—which was then as later the chief beneficiary of the tariff—began to advocate his nomination in 1822 and that his popularity there was expected to be of great importance. In March, 1823, Calhoun wrote: "I stand on the great republican cause free alike from the charge of federalism and radicalism." [1]

[1] 1 Meigs, 296.

That happy medium of non-commitalism, so full of promise to politicians, was what Van Buren's plot was meant to destroy. Even after Calhoun's vote defeated the woollens tariff bill of 1827, many persons thought of him as a nationalist, for he was still popular in Pennsylvania, and had never repudiated his record on internal improvements and protection. But his private letters in the summer of 1827 show that he believed the grasping protectionists were bringing on a crisis and tending "to make two out of one nation"; that he hoped the South would "not be provoked to step beyond strict constitutional remedies"; and that "the great defect in our system" was that "the separate geographical interests are not sufficiently guarded". And he significantly added: "This for yourself."[2] The Vice-Presidency was far from satisfying: as well as earlier and later, he was "burning with passion to be President".[3]

Long before the spring of 1828 he must have

[2] *Corresp.*, 246, 250-51.

[3] 1 Meigs, 423, 424-25. That Calhoun considered his ambition attainable is shown by his correspondence during these years; by his saying, Feb. 15, 1833: "I was [in the summer of 1828] a candidate for reelection on the ticket with General Jackson himself, with a certain prospect of the triumphant success of that ticket, and with a fair prospect of the highest office to which an American citizen can aspire."—2 *Works*, 217.

realized that he could not advance politically unless he let South Carolinians understand that he was an anti-protectionist (for virtually all were opposed to protection) and gained the confidence of the radicals, at least secretly. In 1826, before the Harrisburg convention and the "bill of abominations" had made the tariff question acute throughout the South, a caucus of the South Carolina legislature had nominated Jackson as Presidential candidate for 1828. As there was no likelihood that Calhoun could crowd Jackson out of favor, reëlection as Vice-President was the most that was then attainable. To accomplish this, there were two prerequisites: he must secure at least general political control in South Carolina, so as to prevent too precipitate action, and then unite his forces with those of Jackson.

Like the South Carolina delegation, Calhoun hastened home, where he arrived before the end of May, 1828. He soon informed Duff Green, then one of the most active of the pro-Jackson journalists in Washington, that there was almost unanimity on the Presidential question—there was not "one [Adams] Administration man in fifty"; and the excitement about the tariff was "deep and universal". "In its tendency, I consider it by far the most dangerous question that

has ever sprung up under our system; and mainly
because its operation is so unequal among the
parts. But", he added in words betokening the
officeseeker, "I trust the good sense and virtue of
the people, in which I put my trust, will find a
remedy for this, as they have thus far for all our
political diseases."[4]   This meant that he was
diagnosing the conditions and hoping that the people would, soon or late, summon him as physician
in chief. During that summer and autumn many
politicians consulted him as to what should be
done.   He invariably answered—as he long
afterward wrote in what was really his autobiography, but which he represented as written by another, presumably because the book
was packed with laudations of himself [5]—that

---

[4] 35 *Niles's*, 61.

[5] *Life of John C. Calhoun presenting a condensed History of
Political Events from 1811 to 1843* etc., etc. (N. Y., 1843), 35.
The last paragraph of this sketch says that it was written by
an old friend whose "*statements of fact and opinion he knows to
be entirely authentic.*"   Calhoun wrote to his daughter, Mrs.
Clemson, Feb. 6, 1843: "Mr. Hunter has rewritten most of
the latter [the sketch]; so much so as fairly to be entitled to the
authorship"; and to James Edward Calhoun, Feb. 28th, that this
sketch was "prepared by some of my friends here".—*Calhoun's
Corresp.*, 524-25.   It was soon generally attributed to R. M. T.
Hunter, who seems never to have denied the soft impeachment.
About sixty years later Gaillard Hunt found a letter of Oct. 25,
1854, from Robert Barnwell Rhett (formerly Smith) to Crallé,
the editor of *Calhoun's Works*, saying: "There is but one thing
written by Mr. Calhoun that you ought not to publish as his

he could see but two possible remedies within the limits of the Constitution: one the election of General Jackson, "and the other, State Interposition or Veto, the high remedy pointed out in the Virginia and Kentucky resolutions as the proper one, after all others had failed".[6]

The South Carolina legislature soon appointed electors favorable to Jackson and Calhoun.

Meantime Calhoun, doubting that Jackson, on account of having many protectionist friends, would be likely to secure relief for the South, had begun work on a remedy by "State Interposition or the Veto", his euphemism for *nullification*. At the request of William C. Preston, a prospective member of the South Carolina committee on federal relations, Calhoun gave his views of the situation in the form of a report for that committee. Like Jefferson when he secretly drafted the Kentucky resolutions, Calhoun was Vice-President and ambitious to grasp party leadership as a means of attaining the Presidency, later. Being a candi-

and that is—'*his life*.' He wished me to father it—but I told him that it was impossible for me directly or indirectly to allow any one to understand that I was the author of a publication which I had not written. Hunter and I read it over together in my house in Georgetown. He inserted about a page and a half, and became the putative author" * * *.—Hunt, *Calhoun*, 251.

6 [Calhoun's] *Calhoun*, 35.

date for reëlection on the ticket with Jackson, it was important to conceal his authorship, which for two or three years was only suspected outside of a relatively small circle.[7] He undoubtedly remembered that Jefferson never publicly admitted his connection with the Kentucky resolutions and accordingly was able to profit by them without being the object of criticism. Unquestionable evidence of that connection was not discovered until after Jefferson's death. In December, 1828, the committee, after omitting many passages and making numerous other but not material changes in Calhoun's document, submitted it as their own, together with a protest to the United States Senate, also secretly written by Calhoun.[8] The report was not approved because it contained tenets to which a majority felt that the South Carolina legislature ought not to be committed;[9] but the

[7] Houston, 79; 1 Meigs, 421 ff., 435. See *post* 49 for more on this subject.

[8] 1 Meigs, 377, 378; 6 *Calhoun's Works*, 57-59.

[9] 1 *S. C. Stats. at Large* (ed. Thos. Cooper, 1836), 273; 35 *Niles's*, 309. 1 Meigs, 382, says not approved by either house. Perry, 2 *Reminiscences*, 206; Hayne in his debate with Webster, *Cong. Deb.*, 1829-30, 56; Wm. Drayton, *Oration, July 4, 1831*, p. 12, and many other contemporaries most likely to know agree that it was only *published* by authority. But historical writers of high standing, such as Houston, 86; Ames, 152, 164; Channing, 5 *Hist. U. S.*, 420; McMaster, 5 *Hist. Am. People*, 264n., probably following the often mistaken editor of *Calhoun's Works* (VI, 1) erroneously say that it was adopted by the legislature.

lower house ordered the printing of five thousand copies. The report and the protest (which was approved by both houses) appeared together under the title of "The South Carolina Exposition and Protest on the subject of the Tariff".[10] They were spread broadcast and were popularly accepted as equally official. Even the solemn Calhoun must have found it difficult to suppress laughter when he thought of this, and still more when the protest was presented to the Senate, February 10, 1829, by his old enemy William Smith, who supported it with a very serious speech. As was usual in such cases, this protest was ordered to be printed and was referred to the committee on manufactures, where its repose was undisturbed.

About half of the "Exposition" dealt with the problem of the tariff and contained many sound observations on political economy, on which Calhoun was exceptionally well informed for that time. But his argument had a distinct political bearing. Some of the "Exposition's" leading theses are, that the tariff of 1828 was "unconstitutional, unequal and oppressive, and calculated to corrupt the public virtue and destroy the liberty of the country";[11] "that its burdens are exclu-

10 [Calhoun's] *Calhoun*, 36.

11 The "Exposition" as officially printed is in 1 *S. C. Stats.*

sively on one side and its benefits on the other";
that the duty on imports is a tax that falls on the
exchange and "must, in reality, be paid by the
producer of the articles exchanged"; that the
exportations of the States raising rice, cotton and
tobacco are more than twice those of the other
States, while their population, estimated in Federal numbers, is the reverse; i. e. the South pays
four times as much in taxes as the North; that
the consequent cost of production would deprive
the South of her foreign market, and that if she
should then turn to manufacturing, the North
would make war on slave labor for taking bread
out of the mouths of Northern wives and children;
that through the political connection with the
North, by a perversion of the powers of the Constitution, the South had been stripped of the bless-
ings of nature, which had been converted to the
advantage of the North; that the tariff rears up a
money aristocracy making the rich richer and the
poor poorer and produces "almost universal suffering" in the South; that "on the great and vital
point * * * the interest of the two great sections
is opposed", and "the country is divided and

at Large (1836), 247 ff. Because few persons would be able to
find a copy of this, Calhoun's draft (6 Works, 1-57) is followed
here, and it is both more interesting and more important
historically.

organized into two great parties—the one **sovereign** and the other subject".

But how was the power of the majority to be checked? "No government, based on the naked principle that the majority ought to govern, • • • can preserve its liberty even for a single generation." Construction of the Constitution could not be relied on for defense, for it was sure to be unstable. Safety demanded something stable. This was "found in the reserved rights of the States themselves", that is, sovereignty, which means a right to judge whether delegated powers have been exceeded; and this "clearly implies a veto or control, within its limits, on the action of the General Government, on contested points of authority; and this very control is the remedy which the Constitution has provided to prevent the encroachments of the General Government on the reserve rights of the States" [12] • • •. "It is

[12] The Constitution makes no reference to the subject. Yet in other places Calhoun asserts that nullification is constitutional—in a somewhat Pickwickian sense:—" The committee have thus arrived • • • at the constitutional and appropriate remedy " etc.—6 *Works*, 44. " The committee, having thus established the constitutional right of the States to interpose " etc.—*Ibid.*, 45. Then he says that this, like the power of the Supreme Court to declare a law unconstitutional, " rests on mere inference;—but an inference so clear, that no express provision could render it more certain ".—*Ibid.*, 46. In the letter to Maxcy: • • • " unless the General Government should undertake to oppose force to Constitutional and peaceful remedies ".—1 Meigs, 419. And in

thus effectual protection is afforded to the minority, against the oppression of the majority." A State convention needed only to decide that any act passed by Congress was unconstitutional and then declare it null and void. This, it was held, would be binding alike on the citizens of the State and on the General Government itself, and "place the violated rights of the State under the shield of the Constitution". Such, in substance, was Calhoun's scheme for curing that "great defect in our system" and sufficiently guarding "the separate geographical interests". He insisted that it would certainly protect any State from Federal encroachments in regard to the tariff, slavery or any other question on which a State convention might choose to pass. Yet "the checking or veto power never has * * * been lodged where it was less liable to abuse", for the circumstances of a State convention would be so solemn, deliberate and "favorable to calm investigation and decision". The general recognition of such power would be most beneficent; it would cause moderation on the part of the General Government and a feeling of security on the part of the State, which

the letter to Hamilton: "In the discussion, I have advanced nothing but on the authority of the Constitution itself, or that of recorded or unquestionable facts connected with the history of its origin and formation" etc. See *post* pp. 91, 98, 98n-99n, 114, 129 for more about its being "constitutional".

would replace jealousy and hatred with mutual attachment and patriotism. Hence, ''where there are important separate interests, there is no alternative but a veto to protect them, or the military to enforce the claims of the majority interests''.

If this veto should be unjustly used, so the argument continued, three-fourths of the States could override it by giving the Federal Government, by amendment, authority to pass the act that had been vetoed. That was very different from the provisions of the Constitution, to which this ingenious fiction of a veto was both wholly unknown and antagonistic; for one of the chief purposes of the Constitution was to maintain stability until two-thirds of the Congress should propose amendments, or the legislatures of two-thirds of the States should apply to the Congress to call a convention for proposing amendments, which in either case should be valid only when ratified by the legislatures of three-fourths of the States or by conventions in three-fourths of the States, as the one or the other mode of ratification should be proposed by the Congress.[13] Of course it was not

[13] '' Article V. The Congress, whenever two thirds of both Houses shall deem it necessary, shall propose Amendments to this Constitution, or, on the Application of the Legislatures of two thirds of the several States, shall call a Convention for proposing Amendments, which, in either Case, shall be valid to all Intents and Purposes, as Part of this Constitution, when ratified

explained that the design was to establish a dogma that should do away with the actual prerequisites of amending the Constitution. By the magic of nullification one State should temporarily, and any fraction more than one-fourth of the States— then seven of the twenty-four—should permanently, veto any law of Congress, and, by the same token, any decision of the Supreme Court or any treaty. Obviously this would both alter and vitiate the Constitution.[14] Yet Calhoun urged that it was absurd to expect South Carolina to seek relief according to the constitutional requirements for amendment:

" And ought not a sovereign State, as a party to the constitutional compact, and as the guardian of her citizens and her peculiar interest, to have the power in question [i. e. to nullify]? Without it, the amending power must become

---

by the Legislatures of three fourths of the several States, or by Conventions in three fourths thereof, as the one or the other Mode of Ratification may be proposed by the Congress; Provided that no Amendment which may be made prior to the Year One thousand eight hundred and eight shall in any Manner affect the first and fourth Clauses in the Ninth Section of the first Article; and that no State, without its Consent, shall be deprived of it's equal Suffrage in the Senate."

[14] On this point Madison later wrote to Hayne (*post* 90): " That the 7 might in particular cases be right and the 17 wrong, is quite possible. But to establish a positive and permanent rule giving such a power to such a minority, over such a majority, would overturn the first principle of a free Government and in practice could not fail to overturn the Government itself."—9 *Writings*, 392n.

obsolete, and the Constitution, through the exercise of construction, in the end [become] utterly subverted. * * * How absurd, then, to expect the injured States to attempt a remedy by proposing an amendment to be ratified by three fourths of the States, when, by supposition, there is a majority opposed to them?" [15]

Thus he would put his reasoning above the Constitution.

Although the magnitude of the interests at stake would warrant recommending the call of a constitutional convention at once, it was said, there was a disposition to show "great moderation and forbearance in the exercise even of the most unquestionable right", and "allow time for further consideration and reflection, in the hope that a returning sense of justice on the part of the majority" would lead to a "repeal [of] the obnoxious and unconstitutional acts,—and thereby prevent the necessity of interposing the veto of the State". This course was recommended in expectation that the great political revolution, "which will bring in an eminent citizen [General Jackson], distinguished for his services to his country, and his justice and patriotism, may be followed up, under his influence, with a complete restoration of the pure principles of our Government. But, in thus recommending delay, the committee wish it to be

[15] 6 *Works*, 50-51.

distinctly understood, that neither doubts of the rightful power of the State, nor apprehension of consequences, constitute the smallest part of their motives." [16]

Finally came the warning that, "if the present usurpations and the professed doctrines of the existing system be persevered in,—after due forbearance on the part of the State,—* * * it will be her sacred duty to interpose;—a duty to herself,—to the Union,—to the present, and to future generations,—and to the cause of liberty over the world, to arrest the progress of a usurpation which, if not arrested, must, in its consequences, corrupt the public morals and destroy the liberty of the country." [17]

How strange a mixture of logic, sophistry and dictatorial magniloquence to be secretly written by the Vice-President, when candidate for reëlection, for South Carolina to use against the Federal Government!

With widely varying details, other South Carolinians had previously suggested nullification. In 1827, Turnbull in his *Crisis* had threatened "RESISTANCE"—beginning with remonstrance and, if necessary, going to *"firm resistance"*. [18] He

[16] 6 *Works*, 55-56.
[17] 6 *Works*, 56-57.
[18] *Crisis*, 152.

did not enter into particulars nor employ the word *nullification,* but the logic meant nullification, if the resistance should be successful. This did not look like a peaceable method. Apparently he expected to win by violent threats rather than by violence, but he and the others were fearless. Immediately after the passage of the tariff act of 1828 there was a widespread demand for something decisive, without much danger. Three communications signed "Sidney" and appearing in the Charleston *Mercury* early in July, 1828,[19] employed extreme and biting phrases against the protective tariff and outlined a plan of nullification resembling what was finally adopted. Its temper, like Turnbull's, was passionate and wholly unlike Calhoun's, and the authorship remains unknown. James Hamilton, Jr., was the first to propose in a public speech, at Walterborough, October 21, 1828, a formal method of nullification.[20] Both "Sidney" and Hamilton are supposed to have been in close relations with Calhoun and to have been more influenced by him than he was by them.[21]

[19] Houston, *Nullification,* 75-76.

[20] 35 *Niles's,* 203-209.

[21] Hunt (*Calhoun,* 71) says that Hamilton had been in most intimate relations with Calhoun, "and the idea must have come from Calhoun". Houston thinks that Calhoun put the finishing touches on his " Exposition " about a week after the appearance

Calhoun's "Exposition" was certainly much the most elaborate and plausible scheme for nullification, and it was original and characteristic in style. It well served his immediate purposes—to obtain secret and at least partial control of the radicals and to retain inconspicuous general leadership in South Carolina.

In what was really his autobiography, Calhoun many years later said that he gave Preston permission to tell who was the author of the "Exposition". But the secret was kept within a small circle. In September, 1830, nearly a year before the authorship was generally known, Calhoun wrote to his friend Maxcy: "From a sense of propriety connected with my relations to the General Government, I have not intermingled in the great contest between it and the State, except so far as might seem advisable to direct the eye of the state to the constitution, instead of looking beyond it, for the redress of its [the State's] wrongs." That the act performed, the docu-

---

of "Sidney's" articles, i. e. by July 15th. Hunt infers that Calhoun "worked out his theory" during August and September. But neither submits good evidence for his belief. (Houston, 76; Hunt, *Calhoun*, 71). In drawing his inference from what Calhoun wrote to Monroe, Mr. Hunt seems to have overlooked the important facts that Calhoun was an artful man, was operating secretly and that Monroe was thoroughly hostile to nullification.

ment prepared, was a real service to anyone, few would now maintain. It at least showed that he had entirely changed his position in regard to the constitutionality of the protective tariff. There was, indeed, a difference both of degree and of quality between the tariff of 1816 and that of 1828; but if one was constitutional, the other was not unconstitutional, for both were avowedly for protection. Yet he kept his Northern friends so ignorant of this change, that some of them expected, as will be seen, that when he took his stand it would be against the Nullifiers whom he was actually aiding.

Like Calhoun, George McDuffie joined the nullification movement late, but he soon took a place among the most radical. Where Calhoun was calm, secretive, philosophical, McDuffie was angry, theatrical, revolutionary. His magic resource was oratory. As with many other Nullifiers, McDuffie's first political love had been for the Union, and his graduating oration set forth his belief in its permanency.[22] His little pamphlet on "National and State Rights"[23] is so extremely unionist and anti-secession as to make nationalism seem

[22] O'Neall, 2 *Bench and Bar*, 463-64.

[23] Letters selected by James Hamilton, Jr. from some that McDuffie wrote to the Augusta *Georgia Advertiser* in the summer of 1821. They were published near the end of 1821. The copy cited is a Charleston reprint of 1830.

old and unquestionable, and state-rights novel and absurd. He expressed the uncomplimentary theory that so much was "said on the subject of prostrate state sovereignties and consolidated empire", because "ambitious men of inferior talents, finding they have no hope to be distinguished in the councils of the national government, naturally wished to increase the power and consequence of the state governments, the theatres in which they expect to acquire distinction".[24] In the most indignant terms he denounced the anti-national acts of New England States in connection with the war of 1812, and the attitude of Ohio in relation to the National Bank.[25] As late as 1827 Turnbull attacked him as a nationalist.[26] He soon changed his opinions,—as completely and almost as quickly as he took off his formal black frock and put on homespun, remarking, with the exaggeration of a politician that knows the value of being picturesque and epigrammatic, that broadcloth was fit for only the livery of slaves.[27] He was soon abreast of the alarmists. At the conferences at Hayne's lodgings he agreed with most of Hamilton's opinions.[28] At a banquet, that summer, McDuffie gave this toast:

[24] *National and State Rights*, 12.
[25] *Ibid.*, 22-23. [27] Perry, 2 *Reminiscences*, 205.
[26] *Crisis*, 69-70. [28] 35 *Niles's*, 202.

" The stamp act of 1765, and the tariff of 1828—kindred acts of despotism: when our oppressors trace the parallel, let them remember that we are the descendants of a noble ancestry, and profit by the admonitions of history." [29]

Later, he often and successfully repeated his "forty-bale theory"—meaning that forty out of every hundred bales of cotton raised, or dollars earned, were taken from Southern producers to enrich Northern manufacturers, and he insisted that the producer of exported staples paid the tariff on importations in return. Not content with a sound argument,[30] he could not avoid giving it oratorical, even revolutionary, expression. He said that "no priesthood, in the darkest ages of ignorance and superstition, ever pursued their selfish objects with more untiring perseverance and consummate art, than the manufacturing capitalists have prosecuted their mercenary schemes of monopoly. * * * Aspiring politicians, finding it conducive to their political advancement, have not scrupled to form an alliance, cemented by avarice and ambition, and not less ominous to public liberty than that which has existed * * * between church and state. By the artful use of cant phrases and cabalistic terms, addressed to the

[29] 35 *Niles's*, 61.

[30] Sumner, *Jackson*, 207-09, vigorously defends McDuffie's economic argument.

national pride and local prejudices of the people—such as 'American System' and the 'British System', 'Old England' and 'New England', the 'Free States' and the 'Slave States'—they have succeeded in working up the public mind in the manufacturing States to a state of infatuation almost incredible, and, in my opinion, utterly incurable.'' The sum and substance of this system, he said, was to restrict the Southern States to an intercourse with the tariff States, which reduced them to vassalage; and it was one hundred times more injurious and oppressive than the restrictions which precipitated the Revolution.[31]

It was perhaps still more exciting to South Carolinians to be told that Charleston, "the natural emporium of an extensive foreign commerce, • • • has sunk into comparative insignificance, as a mere place of deposit for our staples of exportations, while the foreign merchandise obtained in exchange for these staples is actually imported by Northern cities''. He believed that, if the Southern States were out of the Union, in less than ten years "the wealth and capital which is [sic] now concentrated in Boston, Providence, Lowell and other great seats of manufacture in the North, would be transferred to Charleston, Savannah,

[31] *Cong. Debates*, 1829-30, 858, 859.

Augusta, Columbia and the other great seats of commerce in the South".[32]

With the visionary, visions are more impressive than facts.

[32] *Cong. Deb.*, 1829-30. The *Crisis*, p. 155, said that but for the tariff, Charleston, which before the Revolution had a greater trade than New York or Philadelphia, would come to its own again.

CHAPTER V

THE WEBSTER-HAYNE DEBATE

For about a year after the campaign of 1828 there was a semi-lull in the excitement, but the leaven of the "Exposition" was rapidly working. South Carolina had voted for Jackson and Calhoun and the Nullifiers were waiting to see if Jackson and the new Congress, to assemble in December, 1829, would do anything to alleviate the conditions.

Nullification had not the slightest direct connection with the resolution that Foot of Connecticut brought into the Senate in December, 1829, instructing the committee on public lands to inquire as to the expediency of limiting for a period the sales to lands that had been put on the market and were subject to entry at the minimum price; and also, whether the office of surveyor-general might not be abolished without detriment to the public interest.[1] Foot probably possessed at least a mild Eastern prejudice against a rapid

[1] *Cong. Deb.*, 1829-30, pp. 3, 4. On Jan. 20, 1830, Foot accepted amendments providing for the abolition of some of the land-offices also, and adding this clause: " or whether it be expedient to adopt means to hasten the sales and extend more rapidly the surveys of the public lands."

development of the West.[2] In any case, the
inquiry seems entirely proper, considering the
actual system: more than seventy-two million
acres of land had been surveyed and offered for
sale at the minimum price of $1.25 an acre,
although at most only one million acres, and usually only half so many, had been sold in any year;
the number of surveyors was needlessly large and
the method of dealing with the lands was elaborate and expensive. Benton attacked the resolution as indicative of the long-standing hostility of
the Northeast to the new States.[3] A spirited,
brief debate between several ensued.

These unexpected occurrences led to the debate
between Webster and Hayne, which was of great
importance in itself and suddenly created intense
national interest in conditions in South Carolina.
Both men were highly picturesque in different
ways and each was largely typical of his State.

Robert Y. Hayne, without any special advantages from education or family, except that he
was a grand-nephew of Isaac Hayne, whom the

[2] Wellington, *Politics and Sectional Influence of the Public
Lands, 1828-42*, 26. Benton asserted that Foot's resolution was
to forestall his (Benton's) graduation bill, which was designed
to hasten the sale of public lands.—*Cong. Deb.*, 1829-30, 118. The
fact that Foot voted against this bill (*Ibid.*, 427) gives color
to Benton's charge, but is far from conclusive.

[3] *Cong. Deb.*, 1829-30, 4.

British executed, had early displayed attractive
manners and excellent talents, which soon helped
him to win uncommon distinction and popularity
as orator, legislator, attorney-general of the State,
and United States Senator. As his first wife was
a daughter of Charles Pinckney and his second a
half-sister of Governor Joseph Alston and a
daughter of Colonel William Alston, a wealthy
rice-planter, his standing, social and political, was
of the best. He had been very active and outspoken wherever slavery was concerned: he com-
manded the troops during the night of the
expected Vesey insurrection and was a member of
one of the courts that tried the conspirators; he
quickly protested against Rufus King's resolution
to use the public lands to aid emancipation and
colonization; he sounded the alarm on account of
the antislavery tendency of the Colonization
Society, and Turnbull gave him the highest praise
for it in the *Crisis;* he insisted that slavery must
be a wholly State question in domestic politics and
a controlling influence in foreign affairs, where
we must shun coöperation with countries like those
of South America, which had marched under ban-
ners proclaiming ''liberty and equality'' and
''universal emancipation'' and were ready to
recognize the independence of Hayti.[4] It is much

[4] Speech on Panama mission, March, 1826, 8 *Benton's Abridgment of Debates,* 426-7.

to his credit that he early favored the abolition of imprisonment for debt, and with clear and forceful arguments attacked the tariff bill of 1824, specially ridiculing the tariff on books.[5] In 1827, Boston merchants opposed to protectionism asked him to present their memorial to the Senate.

Webster already had an assured place among the foremost orators and lawyers of the time. For thirty years the enforcement of the Constitution and the preservation of the Union had been his favorite and most frequent subjects for speeches on public occasions. While in the House he rose to the leadership of the National Republicans. As an antislavery man he had opposed the Missouri Compromise and been conspicuous in the colonization movement. As early as 1820 he publicly expressed doubt of the constitutionality of protectionism.[6] His anti-protection speech of 1824 is still one of the classics of the free-trade school. But, alas, like many another public man, preferring to give up a good argument rather than a good office, he changed his attitude to suit his

[5] Jervey, *Hayne*, 153, 156-57. Jefferson wrote of this tariff on books: " I hope a crusade will be kept up against it, until those in power shall become sensible of this stain on our legislation, and shall wipe it from their code, and from the remembrance of man, if possible."—10 *Writings* (Ford), 293. Unfortunately this hope has not yet been realized.

[6] Hayne quoted the documents (*Cong. Deb.*, 1829-30, 85) showing Webster's attitude in 1820.

constituents and supported the tariff of 1828. He was hardly less inconsistent than Calhoun. Unless Henry Cabot Lodge was wrong, Webster's views on the tariff were controlled by expediency, not deep conviction.[7] By special request he a little later presented to the Senate a petition of the South Carolina Canal and Railroad Company, praying Congress to authorize the Government to subscribe for twenty-five hundred shares of its stock.[8] Thus Webster and Hayne had already been brought into some antagonism, and as exponents of their respective sections strongly resembled Rufus King and Charles Pinckney at the time of the Missouri Compromise.

While sectionalism in 1830 was not so bitter as in 1820, it was perhaps more general: protectionism and antislavery were stronger in the North, anti-protectionism and state-rights had rapidly increased in the South, and the new States were eager to have the General Government speedily dispose of the public lands within their respective borders—to sell them at a nominal price, to give them to actual settlers or even to relinquish them to the interested States. The North and the South each needed the coöperation of the West in order to dominate. During the

[7] *Webster*, 169.
[8] *Cong. Deb.*, 1829-30, 21, 22.

'twenties, the old North had won much favor in the new States by propagating antislavery sentiment in them, by aiding internal improvements and by a high tariff on a few Western products, as has been noticed. But it had opposed any disposition of the public lands that would needlessly hasten the settlement of the trans-Alleghany region, because it would mean a draft on Eastern farms, factories and political power. Although the westward movement was more injurious to the south Atlantic States, especially Virginia and South Carolina, they did not complain much on account of it, for it increased the value of their slaves, and numerous planters took up large tracts in the Southwest, while they or their kinsmen continued to live and be influential in the mother-State. Against such influences, McDuffie's opinions about the evil effects of cheap Western lands met with but little favor in South Carolina; for she was thinking of the tariff and the increasing power and financial resources of the Federal Government and rightly feared that, if the public lands should be slowly sold, the efforts to use the income from them for compensated emancipation and colonization might be successful. Moreover, state-rights ideas predisposed the Nullifiers to favor the claims of the new States to the public lands, and it was hoped that those States would reciprocate by antagonizing consolidation. Yet the Southeast was more opposed to internal improvements than the Northeast was to a rapid disposition of the public lands, perhaps the most general interest of the new States.

Hayne attempted to make political capital for the South both by following up Benton's charges and by criticising the policy of the Government in reserving the public lands as a source of revenue, which, he said, aided consolidation, one of the greatest evils.[9] Everybody knew of the propositions to use this revenue for aiding emancipation and colonization. Hayne later reminded the Senate: "When the proposition was made here to appropriate the public lands to emancipation, I met it with a protest".[10] He endeavored to form a bond of sympathy between the West and the South by likening the burden of debt borne by the land-buyers of the new States to the burden of the Southerners struggling under the system of protection; and he charged that the manufacturing part of the country, the East, wished to restrict the sale of public lands so as to keep an abundance of mechanical laborers near the factories. He thought America ought to remain essentially agricultural for a century to come.

[9] *Cong. Deb.*, 1829-30, pp. 33, 34.
[10] *Cong. Deb.*, 1829-30, p. 83.

This joint effort on the part of Benton and Hayne to prejudice the West against the East to the advantage of the South [11] quickly developed into a serious situation, for the charges contained enough truth to be damaging unless successfully countered. A skilful, vigorous leader was needed. Benton had twice attacked with much more force and originality than Hayne, but if Webster had engaged in a hot debate with Benton, this of itself would have demonstrated that there was a breach in the old alliance between the East and the West. It was much more adroit, as well as less difficult, to accept the challenge from the South. Accordingly, Webster replied, more cleverly than frankly, that, instead of being opposed to the West, it was New England votes that made possible the great Western measures for internal

[11] This was evident at numerous points in the debate and was commonly recognized at the time. J. Q. Adams (8 *Memoirs*, 190) refers to it on the date of Hayne's first speech. In his second speech Hayne said that Webster had hinted at " new alliances to be formed ".—*Cong. Deb.*, 1829-30, 43. See *Ibid.*, 131 for similar reference by Rowan. Hayne and Benton exchanged rather ostentatious compliments (*Cong. Deb.*, 1829-30, 43, 102 ff.), and Webster (*Ibid.*, 59) commented on Benton's praise of Hayne's speech. Judge Smith said, Feb. 26, that Benton " appeared, at the beginning of this debate, to feel great sympathy for the oppressed planters of the Southern States; and some gentlemen hoped that he might probably join the South, and lend his aid to repeal at once the oppressive tariff. But, sir, that hope is gone."—*Ibid.*, 205.

improvements—otherwise it would have been necessary to wait for the Southerns to change their
constitutional notions; that a citizen of Massachusetts, Nathan Dane, had drafted, and the North
alone had passed, the ordinance of 1787, which had
forever fixed the character of the Northwest Ter-
ritory by excluding involuntary servitude. And
he asked if such an ordinance would not have contributed to the greatness of Kentucky. To what
Hayne had said about consolidation Webster
entered his caveat in the words of the members of
the Constitutional Convention of 1787—"the consolidation of our Union, in which is involved our
prosperity, felicity, safety, perhaps our national
existence". And with artful irony he expressed
confidence that Hayne was not and never could be
of those who habitually spoke in disparagement
of the Federal Government and had declared that
it was time to calculate the value of the Union.
This challenge to defend the South Carolina doctrine Hayne accepted, thus unwisely letting his
enemy choose the battle-field. Calhoun, as Vice-
President, could only preside.

At the end of his first speech Webster moved
"the indefinite postponement of the resolution".[12]
Benton seems to have been right in charging that
the "ingenious Senator," Webster, did this to

[12] *Cong. Deb.*, 1829-30, 41.

avoid a direct vote, which might have belied the claim that the East was friendly and the South unfriendly to the West in regard to public lands.[13] In this debate, tactful maneuvering was one of Webster's conspicuous qualities, and his air of triumphant confidence helped him to phenomenal success. Not until he was well advanced in his second long speech—and after Hayne had made several very effective thrusts, especially in regard to public lands, Webster's abandoning a distinguished anti-tariff record and adopting protectionism, his excessive claim for the North in regard to the ordinance of 1787 and his erroneous praise of Nathan Dane — did the famous argument about the Constitution begin. Hayne's impassioned opinions of slavery had made Northern sympathy impossible, and his championing of nullification enabled Webster to turn the discussion from personalities, economics and various sectional interests and prejudices [14] to one between nationality and nullification, be-

13 *Cong. Deb.*, 1829-30, 117.

14 John Quincy Adams referred to the debate before it turned to constitutional questions as " a symptom of the times. Personalities, malignities and hatreds seem to take the place of all enlarged discussion of public concerns."—8 *Memoirs*, 193. Judge Wm. Smith accurately described the personalities between Webster and Hayne (*Cong. Deb.*, 1829-30, 206), and Edward Livingston gave a humorous characterization of the changing variety of the debate.—*Ibid.*, 247.

tween union and disunion, between constitutional order and unconstitutional disorder. Thus nationality was raised as a shield against the blows that nullification and state-rights struck at protection. Pride and patriotism responded in defense of Union, as they would not have done in behalf of the tariff or any State or sectional issue. This made it impossible for many outside of South Carolina to support Hayne in what became the main point of the debate, although the South was strongly for state-rights and against protection, and the South and the West had common views and interests on some phases of the land question.[15] Foot repeated his explanations and Benton persisted in arguments and documents, piling Ossa on Pelion; but the subject of the resolution was rarely mentioned. After four months of interesting debates, or series of argumentative monologues, mainly about the Constitution, nullification and slavery, the whole matter was dropped without a vote.[16] Some of the leading contentions about the Constitution may be cited here.

Hayne called the doctrine of the South Carolina "Exposition" "the good old Republican doctrine of '98," and frequently quoted from Madison and

[15] They voted together on Benton's graduation bill.—Wellington, *Public Lands*, 33.

[16] *Cong. Deb.*, 1829-30, 452.

Jefferson and the Virginia and the Kentucky resolutions. Except one or two surprising errors, he
did not attempt to do more than explain what he
conceived to be the tenets of these documents.[17]
The Constitution being a compact between sovereign States, each of the parties had a right to
judge as to its violation, unless a common judge
had been established. "When it is insisted by the
gentleman that one of the parties (the Federal
Government) 'has the power of deciding ulti-
mately and conclusively upon the extent of its own
authority', I ask for the grant of such a power.
* * * It is not found there" [in the Constitu-
tion].[18] Therefore the power must have been
reserved to the States. "The creating power is
three-fourths of the States. By their decision, the
parties to the compact have agreed to be bound,
even to the extent of changing the entire form of
the government itself; and it follows, of necessity, that, in case of a deliberate and settled difference of opinion between the parties to the compact, as to the extent of the powers of either,

[17] *Cong. Deb.*, 1829-30, 56.

[18] *Cong. Deb.*, 1829-30, 86. Again he erroneously referred to
the General Government as a party to the compact: "A compact
between two, with the right reserved to one to expound the
instrument according to his own pleasure, is no compact at all,
but an absolute surrender of the whole subject-matter to the
arbitrary discretion of the party who is constituted the judge."—
Cong. Deb., 1829-30, 86.

resort must be had to their common superior—
* * * three-fourths of the States."[19]   Hence,
when a State, either through its legislature or a
convention, declared a law of Congress unconstitutional, the Government was bound to halt until
the law should be pronounced constitutional by
three-fourths of the States. This would block the
Government and be a peaceful process, unless
coercion should be attempted. To coercion, resistance "would be just, legal and constitutional".[20]
He was a graceful and eloquent understudy, recit-
ing the leading theses of Calhoun's "Exposition".

Webster's lucidity and conciseness never served
him better than in his summary of this debate. A
few paragraphs from it may suffice:

" Because, if the Constitution be a compact between States,
still that Constitution, or that compact, has established a
government, with certain powers; and whether it be one of
those powers, that it shall construe and interpret for itself
the terms of the compact, in doubtful cases, can only be
decided by looking into the compact, and inquiring what
provisions it contains on this point. Without any inconsis-
tency with natural reason, the government even thus created,
might be trusted with this power of construction. * * *
The gentleman says, if there be such a power of final
decision in the General Government, he asks for the grant
of that power. Well, Sir, I show him the grant—I turn him

[19] *Cong. Deb.*, 1829-30, 89.
[20] *Ibid.*, 91, 92.

to the very words—I show him that the laws of Congress are made supreme; and that the judicial power extends, by express words, to the interpretation of these laws. Instead of answering this, he retreats into the general reflection, that it must result from the nature of things, that the States, being parties, must judge for themselves. * * *

So, then, Sir, even supposing the Constitution to be a compact between the States, the gentleman's doctrine, nevertheless, is not maintainable; because, first, the General Government is not a party to that compact, but a government established by it, and vested by it with the powers of trying and deciding doubtful questions; and secondly, because, if the Constitution be regarded as a compact, not one State only, but all the States, are parties to that compact, and one can have no right to fix upon it her own peculiar construction.

* * * He has not shown, it cannot be shown, that the Constitution is a compact between State governments. The Constitution itself, in its very front, refutes that proposition: it declares that it is ordained and established by the people of the United States. So far from saying that it is established by the governments of the several States, it does not even say that it is established by the people of the several States; but it pronounces that it is established by the people of the United States in the aggregate. The gentleman says, it must mean no more than that the people of the several States, taken collectively, constitute the people of the United States; be it so, but it is in this, their collective capacity; it is as all the people of the United States that they establish the Constitution.

* * * The Confederation was, in strictness, a compact; the States, as States, were parties to it. We had no other General Government. * * * The people were not satisfied with it, and undertook to establish a better. They undertook to form

a General Government, which should stand on a new basis—not a confederacy, not a league, not a compact between States, but a Constitution; a popular government, founded in popular election, directly responsible to the people themselves, and divided into branches with prescribed limits of power, and prescribed duties. They ordained such a government, they gave it the name of a Constitution, and therein they established a distribution of powers between this, their General Government, and their several State governments. When they shall become dissatisfied with their distribution, they can alter it. Their own power over their own instrument remains.

* * * But this is not a treaty, but a constitution of government, with powers to execute itself, and fulfil its duties.

* * * He argues that, if we transgress, each State, as a State, has a right to check us. * * * The gentleman's doctrines would give us a strange jumble of authorities and powers, instead of governments of separate and defined powers.

* * * Finally, Sir, the honorable gentleman says, that the States will only interfere, by their power, to preserve the Constitution. They will not destroy it, they will not impair it; they will only save, they will only preserve, they will only strengthen it! Ah, Sir, this is but the old story." [21]

The peculiar circumstances of the Webster-Hayne debate caused it to be regarded much like a battle by single combat. Had historical accuracy and fair reasoning been the criterion, Edward Livingston's speech would have outranked both Webster's and Hayne's. Livingston's career was already remarkable, and the climax was still in

[21] *Cong. Deb.*, 1829-30, 92-93.

the future. Born in 1764 of a distinguished old New York family and having an elder brother that was a member of the committee of five appointed to draft the Declaration of Independence, his vivid recollections and important associations ran back to the Revolution, and his rich experiences extended from upper New York to the extreme Southwest. He was graduated from Princeton in 1781—the year the Articles of Confederation went into operation, a year before Webster's birth and ten years before Hayne's. He had been practising law four years in New York when the government under the Constitution was inaugurated there. As a citizen of that State he had been in public life (as a Representative in Congress, as United States district attorney and as mayor of New York City) nearly as many years as Webster had spent in Washington; and later as a citizen of Louisiana he had served in one or the other house of Congress almost as long as Hayne had been in the United States Senate. He had been to General Jackson in the War of 1812 what Alexander Hamilton was to General Washington in the Revolution. Being a master of several languages and a profound student of Roman, English, French and Spanish law, he prepared for Louisiana a concise and lucid system of legal practice, helped to codify the law of the State relating to civil rights and remedies, and was author of a penal code that gave him high standing among writers on that subject.[22] Too broad and intelligent for partisan theories, he interpreted the Constitution according to its wording and the logic of the facts that almost compelled its formation and adoption. He condemned both the actual tariff and nullification. Of course he could not match Webster's stately eloquence. His opinions were those of a wise jurist and of a close student and disciple of Madison, the best matter-of-fact expounder of the Constitution. To Livingston, Webster's contention, that the General Government was formed by the people of the United States in their aggregate capacity, seemed as unwarranted as Hayne's, that it was merely the common agent of the States and subject to repudiation by any one of them. According to his philosophy, nullification was not less a revolutionary device than would be a dogma maintaining that the Constitution established a monarchy. And his resumé was a remarkably concise and accurate general characterization of the Constitution, and he carefully explained how violations of it could be lawfully and effectively remedied,—thereby showing that nullification was as lawless an intruder as "Judge Lynch" would be in court.[23]

[22] C. H. Hunt's *Edward Livingston*, 117, 118, 249-50, 255 ff.

[23] " I think ", said Livingston, " that the constitution is the

Because Calhoun's authorship of the "Exposition" was known to only few, although suspected by many, the retributive justice of his dilemma

result of a compact entered into by the several States, by which they surrendered a part of their sovereignty to the Union, and vested the part so surrendered in a General Government.

That this Government is partly popular, acting directly on the citizens of the several States; partly federative, depending, for its existence and action, on the existence and action of the several States.

That, by the institution of this Government, the States have unequivocally surrendered every constitutional right of impeding or resisting the execution of any decree or judgment of the Supreme Court, in any case of law or equity, between persons, or on matters, of whom, or on which, that court has jurisdiction, even if such decree or judgment should, in the opinion of the States, be unconstitutional.

That, in cases in which a law of the United States may infringe the constitutional right of a State, but which in its operation cannot be brought before the Supreme Court, under the terms of the jurisdiction expressly given to it over particular persons or matters, that court is not created the umpire between a State that may deem itself aggrieved, and the General Government.

That, among the attributes of sovereignty retained by the States, is that of watching over the operations of the General Government, and protecting its citizens against their unconstitutional abuse; and that this can be legally done—

First, in the case of an act, in the opinion of the State palpably unconstitutional, but affirmed in the Supreme Court in the legal exercise of its functions,

By remonstrating against it to Congress;

By an address to the people, in their elective functions, to change or instruct their Representatives;

By a similar address to the other States, in which they will have a right to declare that they consider the act as un-

during this debate was but little appreciated: this political Prometheus, who had tried to steal the sacred element of nationality from the Govern-

constitutional, and therefore void;

By proposing amendments to the constitution, in the manner pointed out by that instrument;

And, finally, if the act be intolerably oppressive, and they find the General Government persevere in enforcing it, by a resort to the natural right which every people have to resist extreme oppression.

Secondly, if the act be one of those few which, in its operation, cannot be submitted to the Supreme Court, and be one that will, in the opinion of the State, justify the risk of a withdrawal from the Union, that this last extreme remedy may at once be resorted to.

That the right of resistance to the operation of an act of Congress, in the extreme cases above alluded to, is not a right derived from the constitution, but can be justified only on the supposition that the constitution has been broken, and the State absolved from its obligation; and that, whenever resorted to, it must be at the risk of all the penalties attached to an unsuccessful resistance to established authority.

That the alleged right of a State to put a veto on the execution of a law of the United States, which such State may declare to be unconstitutional, attended (as, if it exist, it must be) with a correlative obligation on the part of the General Government, to refrain from executing it, and the further alleged obligation, on the part of that Government, to submit the question to the States, by proposing amendments, are not given by the constitution, nor do they grow out of any of the reserved powers.

That the exercise of the powers last mentioned would introduce a feature in our Government not expressed in the constitution, not implied from any right of sovereignty reserved to the States, not suspected to exist by the friends or enemies of the constitution, when it was framed or adopted, not warranted by practice, or cotemporaneous exposition, nor implied by the true

ment, while holding the Vice-Presidency and seeking the Presidency, was officially condemned to the torture of silently hearing many thorough refutations of his doctrines.

construction of the Virginia resolutions in '98.

That the introduction of this feature in our Government would totally change its nature, make it inefficient, invite to dissension, and end, at no distant period, in separation; and that, if it had been proposed in the form of an explicit provision in the constitution, it would have been unanimously rejected, both in the convention which framed that instrument, and in those which adopted it."—*Cong. Deb.*, 1829-30, 269-70.

CHAPTER VI

SOME ALLEGED PRECEDENTS FOR NULLIFICATION

It was commonly assumed that the Kentucky and the Virginia resolutions and similar expressions of anti-national opinions in other States were entitled to great weight as interpretations of the Constitution and were good precedents for South Carolina to follow. We may well pause to consider some important facts in several of the leading cases of this kind.

During the Confederation virtual nullification through inaction was so frequent that theorizing about it would have been superfluous. For several decades subsequently, when a State legislature or a political party found its interests in sharp conflict with those of the party in control of the Federal Government, the exercise of ungranted national powers was often alleged. This appealed to State pride, enabled politicians to pose as statesmen, impressed credulous persons and was a ready resource, however brief.

Before 1800, many of the united and unselfish patriots of the Revolution had become jealous rivals and ambitious partisans—the Federalists accusing the Anti-Federalists (Republicans) of wishing to destroy the Constitution and return to the disorderly license of the Confederation, and the Anti-Federalists accusing the Federalists of aiming to restore monarchy or found an oligarchy. One of the best of the Federalists furnished a sad example of this common practice. The success of the Anti-Federalists in New York early in 1799 assured them of a majority of the next State legislature. This was expected to mean the choice of Anti-Federalist Presidential electors and, consequently, "bring Jefferson into the chief magistracy". To prevent "an atheist in religion, and a fanatic in politics, from getting possession of the helm of state", Alexander Hamilton urged Governor John Jay to call the legislature into extra session at once, to change the law so as to provide for the "choosing of electors by the people in districts", instead of by the legislature, and thereby "insure a majority of votes in the United States for a Federal candidate". Happily Jay considered this proposal "a measure for party purposes which I think it would not become me to adopt".[1]

Jefferson's extreme theories of democracy made him suspect that monarchy or tyranny was always concealed in nationalistic tendencies, unless he directed them. And as he had no part in forming the Constitution and felt no sentimental attach-

[1] Hamilton to Jay, May 7, 1800.—10 *Hamilton's Works* (Lodge), 371-74.

ment to it, his ambition, abilities and popularity easily enabled him to become the leader of the Anti-Federalists. At the end of the eighteenth century, political conventions, party platforms and campaign-managers, of the kind that have been common for nearly a century, were unknown. But what is called "viewing with alarm" had long been highly developed and Jefferson was a past master of that artful accomplishment. It was then not rare for a few clever leaders to supply the plans for an approaching campaign, State or national, for often the only approval needful was that of a party caucus or of a majority of a legislature. The alien and the sedition acts—very summary but temporary laws[2] of doubtful constitutionality, passed in 1798 by the Federalists when war with France seemed probable—afforded Jefferson, the Vice-President, eager to supplant President John Adams, a welcome opportunity to draft an indictment against the excessively nationalistic Federalists. Action must be speedy or the most objectionable features would terminate before any party advantage could be gained by decrying them. By Jefferson's secret directions, Madison, John Taylor "of Caroline" and Wilson Cary

[2] The alien law was to be in force but two years and the sedition law until only Mar. 3, 1801.—MacDonald, *Select Documents*, 143-148.

Nicholas in Virginia and John Breckinridge and George Nicholas in Kentucky put through the respective resolutions. Madison's resolutions charged the Federal Government with attempting to enlarge its powers by forced constructions of the Constitution "so as to consolidate the States, by degrees, into one sovereignty, the obvious tendency and inevitable result of which would be, "to transform the present republican system of the United States into an absolute, or, at best, a mixed monarchy"! [3] State legislatures then considered themselves guardians of state-rights, even of state-sovereignty, and Jefferson's indictment was presented where it would be most strongly sup-

[3] 4 *Elliot's Debates,* 528. Excited jealously of Federal authority is still more conspicuous in the " Address to the People," printed *Ibid.,* 529-32. Jefferson, Dec. 11, 1821, wrote to J. Cabell Breckinridge: " At the time when the Republicans of our country were so much alarmed at the proceedings of the Federal ascendancy in Congress [,] in the Executive and the Judiciary departments, it became a matter of serious consideration how head could be made against their enterprises on the Constitution. The leading republicans in Congress found themselves of no use there, browbeaten as they were by a bold and overwhelming majority. They concluded to retire from that field, take a stand in their state legislatures, and endeavor there to arrest their progress. The Alien and Sedition laws furnished the particular occasion. The symapathy between Va. and Ky. was more cordial and more intimately confidential than between any other two States of republican policy."—Warfield, *Ky. Resolutions of 1798,* 138. At first he thought that the N. C. legislature would be the best place to start the movement.—Warfield, 146, 148.

ported. He expected that other legislatures could then be easily aroused against the Federalists.

His draft of the Kentucky resolutions of 1798 declared the Constitution a compact, and "to this compact each State acceded as a State, and is an integral party", and "has an equal right to judge for itself, as well of infractions as of the mode and measure of redress"; that "where powers are assumed which have not been delegated, a nullification of the act is the right remedy; that every State has a natural right in cases not within the compact (*casus non foederis*), to nullify of their own authority all assumptions of power by others within their limits".[4] The extravagance of Jefferson's attitude was manifested by his saying that the acts criticised were "so palpably against the Constitution as to amount to an undisguised declaration that that compact is not meant to be the measure of the powers of the General Government; but that it will proceed in the exercise over these States of all powers whatsoever" etc. And he expected that the "co-States recurring to their natural right, in cases not made federal, will concur in declaring these acts void and of no force, and will each take measures of its own for providing that neither these acts, nor any others of the

4 Warfield, *Ky. Resolutions of 1798*, 152, 156.

general government, not plainly and intentionally authorized by the Constitution, shall be exercised within their respective territories."[5]   Although these sentences clearly asserted the right of nullification by individual States, Jefferson evidently intended them for political effect and merely to secure legislative resolutions *expressing the opinion* that the hated laws were unconstitutional and therefore of no effect, but not to call for legislation to nullify the laws; and actual nullification by a State singly was wholly foreign to his purpose.[6]

[5] Warfield, 158-59. Thirty-four years later Madison, who was a devoted admirer of Jefferson and was too much influenced by him in 1798, suggested: "Allowances also ought to be made for a habit in Mr. Jefferson as in others of great genius of expressing in strong and round terms, impressions of the moment."—9 *Madison's Writings* (Hunt), 479.

[6] "For the present, I should be for resolving the alien and sedition laws to be against the constitution and merely void, and for addressing the other States to obtain similar declarations; and I would not do anything at this moment which should commit us further, but reserve ourselves to shape our future measures or no measures, by the events which may happen."—To John Taylor, Nov. 26, 1798, 7 *Writings* (Ford), 311.

"Suppose you were instead of the invitation [to the other States] to coöperate in the annulment of the acts, to make it an invitation 'to concur with this commonwealth in declaring, as it does hereby declare, that the said acts are, and were *ab initio*, null, void and of no force, or effect.' I should like it better."—To Wilson C. Nicholas, Nov. 29, 1798, 7 *Writings* (Ford), 312-13.

After the Kentucky and the Virginia resolutions had been

The Kentucky legislature in its resolutions of 1798 rejected Jefferson's extreme phrases. But, surprised and irritated by the sharp criticisms that those resolutions occasioned, it declared, in its resolutions of 1799, that "a nullification by those sovereignties of all unauthorized acts done under cover of that instrument is the rightful remedy".[7] This was Jefferson's idea concisely expressed.

Madison's Virginia resolutions of 1798 were fathered in the house of delegates by John Taylor, whose radicalism exceeded Jefferson's as much as Jefferson's exceeded Madison's.[8] As proposed and

sharply criticised by other States, he again wrote to Wilson C. Nicholas, Sept. 5, 1799, that something should be done to preclude the inference of acquiescence, and that there should be a firm protest "against the precedent and principle [of the alien and the sedition acts], and *reserving* the right to make this palpable violation of the federal compact the ground of doing in [the] future whatever we might now rightfully do. * * * Mr. M[adison] who came, as had been proposed, does not concur in the *reservation* proposed above; and from this I recede readily, not only in deference to his judgment, but because as we should never think of separation but for repeated and enormous violations, so these, when they occur, will be cause enough of themselves."—7 *Jefferson's Writings* (Ford), 390-91.

7 Warfield, 125-26.

8 Taylor wrote to Jefferson near the end of Nov., 1798, before the Va. resolutions were proposed: "If a sufficient spirit had appeared in our legislature, it was my project, by law to declare the unconstitutional laws of Congress void, and as that would have placed the State and general government at issue, to have submitted the point to the people in convention, as the

for some time debated, these resolutions contained a phrase declaring the alien and sedition
acts "unconstitutional, and not law, but utterly
null[,] void and of no power or effect".[9] To
avoid the charge that the resolutions were designed to nullify the alien and sedition acts, all of
the phrase following "unconstitutional" was
stricken out.[10] The resolutions as passed were
milder and less clear than those of Kentucky; they

only referee. This measure seemed to be opposed properly to
all those which have invested one man with despotic powers;
for as it was the custom of the Roman aristocracy, whenever
it felt itself in danger, to appoint a dictator, to see that the
commonwealth sustained no injury, so the same office seemed to be
peculiarly proper for a convention is [in?] a popular republic.
Besides it was a measure calculated to attach to the real republicans the physical power of the State. It was however only a
provisional project, and as you seem to disapprove of pushing
on at present to this ultimate effort, I will forbear the attempt.
Indeed there is yet but little prospect of its success."—2 *John
P. Branch Historical Papers*, 277.

9 In April, 1830, Madison was unable to recollect, and he had
not preserved any written evidence to show, whether that phrase
was his or not.—9 *Madison's Writings* (Hunt), 388 note. It
seems unlikely that Taylor would have added it without Madison's
consent.

10 Taylor had concluded to favor what was designed to be " only
an appeal to public opinion."—Benton, 1 *Thirty Years' View*,
351. And Madison, many years later, said that the words were
omitted because " regarded as only surplusage," and it was
feared " lest they should be misconstrued into a nullifying import
instead of a declaration of opinion ", and the word *unconstitutional* alone retained as more safe against that error.—9 *Madison
Writings* (Hunt), 388-89.

avoided the words *null* and *nullify* and employed the vague word *interpose*. The vote in the upper house was 14 to 3, but in the lower house it was 100 to 63.[11] The members of this strong opposition— a change of 19 votes would have defeated the resolutions—issued an address in vindication of the alien and sedition acts.[12]

The legislatures that replied to the Kentucky and the Virginia resolutions of 1798 perceived very little difference between them. Six legislatures regarded one or both States as attempting to usurp the powers of the Supreme Court in declaring the alien and sedition acts unconstitutional.[13] Nine legislatures condemned and not one (except Kentucky, of course) approved of the Virginia resolutions.[14] Although the Kentucky resolutions received the unanimous vote of the senate, and only one member in the house was opposed to all of them,[15] they were condemned by the legislatures of eight States.[16] Thus the Kentucky and the Virginia resolutions, sent to all the States to obtain aid and comfort, received not one favorable

11 Warfield, 104.

12 Ames, 16.

13 See Ames, 17 (Rhode Island), 19 (Mass.), 20 (Pa.), 25 (N. H.), 26 (Vt.).

14 Ames, 16. In Pa. only the lower house passed resolutions.

15 Warfield, 94.

16 Ames, 16. In one or two States only one house voted.

response.   Yet this meant much less than the words imply; for in nearly every case the legislatures that condemned these resolutions had Federal majorities, while their Anti-Federalist minorities approved of all except the extreme features of the resolutions.[17]

Jefferson and John Taylor, radicals, not constitutionalists, had supplied the theories that the Nullifiers needed. Even if the Kentucky and the Virginia resolutions had come out squarely for nullification, that would not have meant much, considering their origin and purpose and the serious condemnation they aroused. It is one of the great anomalies of American history that these partisan resolutions of two State legislatures should be considered so much more weighty than the partisan counter-resolutions of several times as many State legislatures denouncing them. They ought to be known as a classical warning against proving rules by exceptions. Moreover, Virginia and Kentucky each subsequently on various occasions condemned opinions sufficiently similar to those of 1798 and 1799 to be a repudiation of anything even resembling nullification.[18] The Kentucky and the Virginia resolutions were

[17] Prof. F. M. Anderson (5 *Amer. Hist. Rev.*, 45 ff., 225 ff.) shows that party lines were followed in nearly all cases.
[18] Ames, 158-161.

thoroughly political propaganda for the Anti-Federalists.[19] The Virginia resolutions of 1798 became the Republican platform of 1799 in Virginia.[20] In the campaign of 1800, the Kentucky and the Virginia resolutions and Madison's report on the replies to the Virginia resolutions were used in several States as a source from which to draw partisan arguments. The campaign-book that each party has long issued before every Presidential election, was a much later development.[21] And Jefferson and Madison were much like campaign managers, Madison acting partly, and Jefferson wholly, in secret. Such are not the

[19] The highest authority on the Ky. resolutions of 1798 says that they " were of the nature of a political manifesto; * * * they were also intended to invite coöperation and gauge the political feeling throughout the country. * * * Thus their platform, for it was very like a party platform, naturally tended to present a maximum policy, and to declare a willingness to go to the greatest length to which they could possibly be driven." The " end and aim being agitation ", it " spoke rhetorically, declaring in heightened metaphors the facts that would have stirred up few to listen if couched in simple language ".—Warfield, 166-68.

[20] Ambler, *Sectionalism in Va.*, 77.

[21] Calhoun regarded the resolutions as so distinctly a campaign issue that he spoke of the success of the election of 1800 as " the implied sanction which a majority of the States gave, in the important political revolution which shortly followed, and brought Mr. Jefferson into power ".—6 *Works*, 44. And again: " The great struggle that preceded the political revolution of 1801, which brought Mr. Jefferson into power, turned essentially on it " [the relation between the States and the General Government] * * *. —*Ibid.*, 60.

circumstances in which constitutions receive true expositions. But the Nullifiers, needing precedents, assumed that the resolutions of 1798 and 1799 were as authoritative as any part of the Constitution.

When the legislature of Pennsylvania, in 1809, passed resolutions in regard to the long-pending Olmstead case—a conflict between Federal and State authority—proposed an amendment to the Constitution for the establishment of an impartial tribunal "to determine disputes between the general and state governments", and sent these resolutions to the several States, not one State agreed with them and at least eleven States condemned them. Among these eleven were Maryland, North Carolina, Georgia, Tennessee and Kentucky. The answering resolutions of the Virginia general assembly were especially elaborate, rational and, in spirit, antagonistic to the doctrines of 1798-99. And they gave an effective reply to such arguments as Hayne's and Calhoun's about the danger of permitting any part of the Federal Government to decide questions concerning the rights of a State.[22]

[22] Ames, 45 ff., gives a long summary and the most important documents. C. W. Loring (*Nullification, Secession* etc., 118-23) gives a very clear summary of the whole historical incident and

During the unpatriotic, anti-national movements in New England, 1808-15, occasioned by the
embargo and the non-intercourse act and culmi-
nating in the doctrines of the Hartford convention, theories of state-sovereignty, state-allegiance
and kindred subjects, essential to the logical development of nullification, were employed but usually
in rather inchoate forms, for matters were not
pressed to extremities.[23] The amendments to the
Constitution proposed by the Hartford convention, endorsed by Massachusetts and Connecticut,
and largely designed to enable a small minority of
States to thwart the will of a majority, met with
no more favor than the Kentucky and the Virginia

shows how Presidents Jefferson and Madison, in turn, were associated with some features of the case and, of course, in a very
different light from that of 1798-99.

[23] In most cases it was attempted, as in S. C. later, to represent
the Government under the Constitution as being about what it had
been under the Articles of Confederation. The general assembly of
R. I., 1809, held that it was its duty to interpose to protect
the people from unconstitutional acts of the Federal Government.
Ames, 43-44, gives the text. For the attitude of Conn., later,
see Ames, 61, 76. The Pa. resolutions of 1811 against the U. S.
Bank called the Federal Constitution "an act of union * * * to
all intents and purposes a treaty between sovereign states".—
Ames, 53. The general court (general assembly) of Mass. in
1814 called the embargo "unconstitutional and void" and employed phrases from the Va. resolutions and cited Madison's
opinions about interposing, in contrast with what he was doing
as President.—Ames, 71-75, gives the text. The report of the
Hartford convention contains a similar passage. — Dwight's
Hartford Conv., 361.

resolutions: no other New England State approved of them, and Vermont, New York, New Jersey, Pennsylvania, Virginia, North Carolina, Ohio, Tennessee and Louisiana disapproved of them, some very bitterly.[24] The South Carolina legislature rebuked the attitude of New England in 1812 and the Hartford Convention was generally execrated and called traitorous.[25]

As we know, the Kentucky and the Virginia resolutions, like those of the New England States, were never carried out because they were chiefly for political effect or some temporary purpose. Unexpected condemnation of them soon caused them to be laid aside and almost forgotten. But in South Carolina conditions were peculiar: the people were very excitable and credulous; the leaders were audacious and foresaw how nullification, if recognized, could be used to shield other interests of the State that were much more important than those involved in the protective tariff. And Calhoun believed that he could slip on Jefferson's political clothes of 1798-1800 and, soon or

[24] Ames, 86-88.

[25] Houston, *Nullification*, 25. "There was not a man among us who did not pronounce the Hartford Convention a traitorous association; indisputably it becomes us to look well to it, that we do not tread in the very footsteps which we have denounced with so much bitterness."—Ex-Gov. David R. Williams, quoted in 6 *Political Science Quarterly*, 237.

late, walk into the White House.[26]   Jefferson had
died in 1826, but with the prestige of his name
and of the magnified traditions of the Kentucky
and the Virginia resolutions the Nullifiers expected to launch and to lead a far-reaching and
compelling movement for nullification as a fundamental principle of the Constitution.[27]

But what did the venerable James Madison say?
He was one of the most influential members of the
Constitutional Convention of 1787, reporter of its
proceedings, author of the Virginia resolutions
and of the long report on them to the Virginia
legislature of 1799-1800.   For more than two score
years he had been the best informed and the most
respected interpreter of the intended meaning of
the Constitution.   Since the appearance of the
"South Carolina Exposition" and especially since
the Webster-Hayne debate, public men on both
sides—Webster, Everett, Livingston, Hayne and
numerous others of less fame—had sought his

26 "You will see ", Calhoun wrote in Aug., 1831, " that I place
myself on the principles that brought the Republican party into
power in 1801 " * * *.   " Mine are the opinions of the Republican
party of '98, beyond which I do not go an inch."—*Corresp.*,
296, 298.

27 Soon after the debate with Webster, Hayne wrote to Hammond: " If our friends at home could be induced to base their
proceedings on the Virginia Resolutions of '98, I am confident
they will carry with them the whole South, and a large portion
of the people in other quarters."—6 *Am. Hist. Rev.*, 737.

opinion. Madison surprised Hayne, who also sent a copy of his speeches against Webster, with a thoroughgoing refutation of the claim that the Virginia resolutions were a precedent for South Carolina.[28] This and other letters were soon published or handed about, fully two years before the nullification convention.[29] But Calhoun, Hayne (after that refutation) and the other Nullifiers acted as if they had never heard of Madison, whose opinions were often quoted and greatly strengthened the Nationalists and the Southern Unionists.

[28] 9 *Madison's Writings* (Hunt), 383n. ff., gives the letter. Hayne received and "promised to answer my letter, but never did ".—4 *Madison's Writings* (Congressional edition), 232.

[29] Perhaps Madison's most concise and epigrammatic statement was in his letter of May 8, 1830, to Edward Livingston: "The error in the comments on the Virginia proceedings has arisen from a failure to distinguish between what is declaratory of opinion and what is *ipso facto* executory; between the right of *the parties* to the Constitution and of a *single* party; and between resorts within the purview of the Constitution and the *ultima ratio* which appeals from a Constitution, cancelled by its abuses, to original rights paramount to all constitutions."—4 *Writings* (Cong. ed.), 80.

CHAPTER VII

NULLIFIERS VS. UNIONISTS, 1830-32.—CALHOUN'S ATTITUDE

Before the summer of 1830 the Nullifiers, confident that Congress would do nothing to lower the tariff, began a vigorous agitation in favor of a State convention, "where the people in their sovereign capacity should decide what ought to be done". They denounced as timid submissionists, afraid to trust the people, all persons that hesitated. Nearly all argued with at least the presumption and many, like Calhoun, with the positive assertion, that the proper and constitutional [1] method of settling questions of usurpation of power on the part of the General Government belonged to each State in its sovereign convention. But being adroit campaigners, they formed what they called the "State-Rights and Free-Trade" party and kept nullification in the background as only a possibility, although "peaceful, safe and efficacious".[2] State-rights and free-trade clubs

[1] *Ante* pp. 42n, 43n and *post* 98, 98n-99n, 129.

[2] "I go on further to show that the proposed remedy is a peaceful, safe and efficacious one, and less liable to abuse than any check that ever was devised in government. We propose, in effect, that one-fourth of the States have a right of annulling

soon multiplied. On gala and sale days oratorical "fire-eaters," as their opponents dubbed them, harangued the crowds about the injustice of the tariff, the consequent misfortunes and the total failure of several years of petitioning and protesting. South Carolina had been wronged, humiliated, oppressed, enslaved, but by insisting on her rights she could recover her naturally superior economic advantages. Lest anyone should think nullification dangerous, and to inspire courage, Turnbull cried: "Look again to Georgia, she has not once but twice vanquished the Federal Government, and so will it be with us".[3] Thus, as James L. Petigru described the campaign, the land of the producer was filled with baleful images of ruin and tyranny and boundless exaggeration.[4]

any act of the General Government, on the ground of its unconstitutionality; and that for the purpose of compelling the majority to appeal to the three-fourths for a grant of power which is denied, any State may suspend the operation of the act within its own jurisdiction."—*The Remedy by State Interposition, or Nullification;* explained and advocated by Chancellor Harper in his speech at Columbia, September 20, 1830 (Charleston, 1832) p. 16.

[3] *Proceedings of the State Rights Celebration at Charleston, July 1, 1830,* p. 43.

[4] Capers, *Memminger,* 63. This great lawyer and eccentric wit wrote about this time: "I am devilishly puzzled to know whether my friends are mad, or I beside myself. * * * That we are treated like slaves, that we are slaves in fact, that we are

The leaders of the Unionists were men of high character, great ability and, what is rarer, of statesmanlike judgment—Joel R. Poinsett, Hugh S. Legaré, James L. Petigru, William Drayton, Daniel E. Huger, Thomas S. Grimké, Benjamin F. Perry, Chancellor Henry William DeSaussure and his son Henry A., Judges John Peter Richardson, David Johnson and John Belton O'Neall. Before the end of 1830 Judge William Smith took his stand with them.[5] Among comparatively few youthful enthusiasts in this party were William

worse than slaves and made to go on all fours, are stories that seem to me very odd, and make me doubt whether I am not under some mental eclipse, since I can't see what is so plain to others. * * * And, although I do not myself subscribe to the plan, I am fain to confess many excellent men have thought that the making a hell upon earth is a good way of being sure of a place in heaven."—Carson, *Petigru*, 79-80.

[5] His speech on Foot's resolution, Feb. 26, 1830 (*Cong. Debs.*, 1829-30, 196-210) was in hearty sympathy with the anti-tariff movement and even with the anti-tariff writings of Turnbull and Cooper, but was clearly antagonistic to Hayne, and expressed the belief that tariff reform would come in a constitutional manner. He avoided the subject of nullification. His letter of Nov. 10, 1830, " To the Good People of South Carolina " (published in the Charleston *Courier*, Nov. 13, and 15, 1830) showed where he stood. Then and later he explained the needlessness and unconstitutionality of nullification, exposed the inconsistencies between the opinions that Calhoun, McDuffie, James Hamilton, Jr., and other Nullifiers were expressing at this time and those expressed when favoring protection and internal improvements.—Speech at Spartanburg, Aug. 1, 1831 (Camden, S. C., 1831).

Gilmore Simms, editor of the Charleston *City Gazette* and a promising man of letters, and C. G. Memminger, thirty years later to become the Confederate Secretary of the Treasury. Charleston alone had three Union newspapers—The *Courier,* the *Southern Patriot* and the *City Gazette.* Each contained a stream of argumentative contributions, often in series, and well reasoned editorial articles against nullification. "Gallatin," in the *Courier,* made many a skilful thrust at the radicals. "The band of nullifiers," he wrote, "cannot distinguish between the Government of the Union, *as formed,* and the *antecedent relation* in which the thirteen States stood to each other. They cannot perceive that the *aggregate sovereignty* of the nation under the Constitution, is an emanation from the independent States, which of their own free will and accord deprived themselves of a part of their respective sovereignties, *with no allusion to, or stipulation of* the circumstances under which it could be *taken back.*" [6] "It may well be asked", wrote "Lucius", "if this doctrine [of nullification] be true, why have we not heard it before?" How did it escape the eagle eye of Patrick Henry?

[6] *Courier,* Aug. 3, 1830. He also answered the call for a convention by saying: "As nullification conceals disunion, so both are disguised under a call for a Carolina convention."— *Courier,* Aug. 24, 1830.

Why did neither Hamilton, Madison nor Jay mention it?[7] In the South Carolina house of representatives D. E. Huger reasoned most impressively against nullification and gave almost pathetic warnings of the folly of the aims of the radicals.[8] If the Nullifiers had been susceptible to facts and reason, they would early have been routed by the numerous correct explanations of the Constitution and the exposures of nullification.[9]

The Unionists appreciated Webster's patriotic eloquence and fine sentiments, but his easy conversion to protection and his assertion that the Constitution was "established by the people of the United States in the aggregate" greatly embarrassed them.[10] By frankly admitting the injustice of the tariff and the dangers of consoli-

[7] *Courier*, Aug. 3, 1830.

[8] *Debate in the S. C. Legislature, 1830*, 32-48. An anti-nullification speech that Thomas S. Grimké delivered in the S. C. senate in Dec., 1828, was published in 1830 and was worthy the highest praise on account of its nationalism.—Charleston *Courier*, Dec. 15 and 20, 1828; Feb. 19, 1830.

[9] Prof. Boucher, *Nullification Controversy*, 68-79, gives a very lucid and instructive summary of the theories of the Unionists about the Constitution.

[10] An editorial article in the Unionist *Southern Patriot*, Mar. 9, 1830, expressed this representative opinion: Although there was no disputing Webster's "transcendent abilities," some parts of his speech showed "more of the dexterity of the advocate than the ingenuous spirit of the impartial debater."

dation, they displayed moral courage that made more effective their ridicule of McDuffie, Governor Hamilton and others for being so violent and revolutionary against what, in principle but not in equal degree, they had previously favored.[11] Although Charleston was a little city with only a small foreign-born population and relatively few artisans, Unionist appeals were made to *citoyens* and to *Landsleute*, in their mother-tongues, and to mechanics.[12]

Even this campaign of 1830 was so intense, according to Judge Smith, who had been active in politics for about forty years, that the State was thrown into a violent ferment. Former political associations were broken up, business was neglected, intimate friendships were severed and bitter reproaches were cast upon those who dared to think for themselves.[13] The Nullifiers elected only

[11] Hamilton explained at great length how he came to write the introduction to McDuffie's pamphlet on " National and State-Rights " (*Ante* p. 50), and said that he had changed his opinions because he had learned from experience that the Government was run to serve selfish and sectional interests. He likened his case to that of a planter taking an overseer on recommendation and later discovering that the overseer was abstracting rice.—*Courier*, Aug. 23, 1830.

[12] *Courier*, Aug. 16, Sept. 2 and 6, 1830; Aug. 31, 1831; Charleston, *Southern Patriot*, Oct. 8, 1832. The Mechanics held a Union and State Rights meeting.—*Southern Patriot*, Oct. 4, 1832.

[13] " To the Good People of South Carolina." Charleston *Courier*, Nov. 15, 1830.

a majority of the legislature, whereas two-thirds was required for calling a convention.

As keeping nullification in the background had not brought the desired success, the agitation was both diversified and intensified, with determination to elect a two-third majority, in 1832. First, the actions of Congress during the session from December, 1830, to March, 1831, were to be closely watched and boldly exposed. Then, wrote Governor Hamilton, the commander-in-chief of nullification, to his journalistic lieutenant at Columbia, James H. Hammond, we will put a little fire into the columns of the sluggish Charleston *Mercury,* the leading organ of the Nullifiers, and "begin to say something of our means of redress,—and what is left for South Carolina to do for herself".[14] Much was made of social features: there were parades with special uniforms and conspicuous wearing of the blue cockade, as an emblem of state-sovereignty; dinners with a rapid fire of daring toasts and sensational speeches about resisting oppression and refusing to be slaves; dramatic exhibitions and fancy balls with a maximum of color, display of State pride and reckless sentiment. In vain did the Unionists attempt to rival such demonstrations: their dinners, attended

[14] 6 *Amer. Hist. Rev.,* 740-41.

by the most honored and dignified men in the
State, were feasts of reason where arguments
were both unanswerable and made no converts;
their parades were perfunctory marches of grave
men conscientiously trying to check the dangerous
folly of the time,—while the sons of many of them
paraded, drank and shouted with the Nullifiers.

One of the most important of those dinners
where Nullifiers strove to outdo one another in
hardy sententiousness was given to McDuffie in
Charleston, May 19, 1831. It was evidently
planned and managed by Governor Hamilton, who
well knew McDuffie's fiery quality.[15] The extreme
radicals could have found no more typical spokesman than McDuffie. He considered the idea ridicu-
lous that the contest might lead to bloodshed and
civil war, but he was not to be frightened in any
case. And he frankly declared it a solecism to
suppose that nullification was constitutional. ''The
right flows from a higher source.''[16] He was a
clear-minded, logical revolutionist.

[15] Two weeks before the dinner, Hamilton wrote that he expected soon to see McDuffie and have '' a full consultation with
our friends,'' and that '' we must have a rally on some firm
ground and then stand manfully to our arms ''. Two days after
the speech, he reported that McDuffie had been ''almost seemingly
inspired,'' and was Hamilton's guest while carefully revising
the speech to be '' circulated in pamphlet form throughout the
South.''— 6 *Am. Hist. Rev.*, 745, 746.

[16] Yet at that dinner one of the toasts read, in part: '' Nulli-

Both parties held ambitious and festive celebrations in Charleston on the Fourth of July, 1831—the fifty-fifth anniversary of the signing of the Declaration of Independence. McDuffie having spoken as the leaders desired, a few weeks earlier, Hayne was chosen to announce to the public the purpose to apply nullification if nothing less should suffice. He made a good popular appeal and did it with moderation.[17] For once the Unionists outshone their rivals, thanks to the day, the presence of several aged and enthusiastic veterans of the Revolution and the speeches and letters contributed by the most representative opponents of nullification. Drayton's formal oration was a skilful refutation of the "Exposition." Legaré, Petigru and General James Blair were especially keen.[18] The youthful poet-editor William Gilmore Simms recited "Our Union—A National Ode".[19]

fication—The only rightful remedy of an injured State. In itself, peaceful and constitutional."—Meigs, 1 *Calhoun*, 430-32, quotes both McDuffie and the toast.

[17] Jervey (*Hayne*, 287-89) and Meigs (1 *Calhoun*, 433-34) give the substance of it.

[18] The proceedings were published in a pamphlet of 104 pages: "An Oration * * * Charleston, * * * July 4, 1831. By The Hon. William Drayton. To which is annexed an account of the Celebration of the 55th Anniversary of American Independence, by the Union and State Rights Party. Charleston, S. C., 1831." Capers reprinted most of it.

[19] Its keynote was—

"Breathes there a man with soul so dead,

Among the best of the numerous patriotic toasts at the banquet were his, "The State of our Union and the Union of our States: What God hath put together let no man put asunder", and Grimké's, "The Union: We will calculate its value when we have forgotten its founders."[20]

President Jackson sent a letter of June 14, 1831, expressing "pride in calling myself a citizen [of South Carolina] by birth." With unwonted mildness the brusque old soldier undertook to calm the disaffection and in words from Washington's "Farewell Address" gently cooed of the beloved Union. What was supposed to be more significant was his "pointing to the fast approaching extinction of the public debt, as an event which must necessarily produce modifications in the revenue system, by which all interests, under a spirit of mutual accommodation and concession, will be probably protected."[21]

> Who never to himself hath said,
> This is my own, my native land!"

The poem concludes with this reply to Dr. Cooper's suggestion about calculating the value of the Union—

> " Let him who sees all this—the fruit
> From our proud Union's glorious root—
> The offspring of whatever state—
> Let him come forth and calculate
> Its value—if he can! "

> —Drayton, 72-79; Capers, 70-75.

[20] Capers, 94-105.   [21] Capers, 47.

The temper of the Nullifiers was manifested by their attitude toward this letter. Governor Hamilton protested against it, and the legislature, in December, 1831, approved a long report containing these contemptuous sentences, with capitalization (or the lack of it) and paragraphing to match:

"Is this legislature to be schooled and rated by the President of the United States?

"Is it to legislate under the sword of the Commander-in-Chief? * * *

"The executive of a most limited government; the agent of an agency, but a part of a creature of the states, undertakes to prescribe a line of conduct to a free and sovereign State, under a denunciation of pains and penalties." Of course it is the President's duty to enforce the laws, and South Carolina would help. But if South Carolina, acting in her sovereign capacity, decides that any enactment of Congress is unconstitutional— "that judgment is paramount; and if the executive, or all the combined departments of the General Government, endeavor to force such [an] enactment, it is by the law of tyrants, the exertion of brute force." [22] That was what the excited leaders wished to be the question; and they had

[22] 1 *S. C. Stats. at Large* (1836), 307, 308.

long been assuring the people that it was the question.

From about the end of 1828, when the general character of the "Exposition" became known, there was a persistent rumor that Calhoun was its author. But this was often denied, and he had not publicly shown where he stood, except that he was opposed to the woollens bill, as indeed many protectionists were. This lack of frankness had occasioned much comment and inquiry. That his change of opinion was strongly suspected by many Unionists was evinced by the significant wording of one of the regular toasts at their semi-centennial celebration:

" The Vice-President of the United States: His political intimates have declared their sentiments on Nullification,—will *he shrink* from an *open* exposition of his own?" [23]

More, rather than less, than formerly Calhoun had been brooding over his Presidential prospects. It had been supposed that Jackson would care for only one term, and Calhoun had confidently hoped to succeed him. But before this time Jackson was known to desire reëlection, had chosen Van Buren as a favorite and political heir and had also begun a bitter attack on Calhoun on account of Calhoun's supposed attitude as Secretary of War

[23] Drayton, 51; Capers, 43.

toward Jackson's high-handed actions in Florida, many years previously. Of the leading Presidential aspirants, Clay was the champion of the tariff. Jackson held a middle course, drawing considerable support from both protectionists and anti-protectionists. Notwithstanding many unfavorable conditions, Calhoun believed that his own prospects were good. He not only "lusted for the Presidency" but he was also confident that he alone was fit for it: he privately berated his rivals and fairly groaned: "Universal discontent, distraction and corruption seem to be taking possession of the country." [24]

When returning home from Washington in March, 1831, Calhoun halted at Columbia and held a private conversation with James H. Hammond, who was in only less confidential relations with Calhoun than with Hamilton.[25] Calhoun said that General Jackson was losing the confidence of his party everywhere; that the delegations of Tennessee,[26] Kentucky, Pennsylvania and Virginia (except Stevenson and Archer) and three-fourths

[24] Whoever wishes the details should read his *Correspondence*, 290-321.

[25] Hammond's careful record of this conversation is printed in 6 *Amer. Hist. Rev.*, 741-745, and in Meigs, 1 *Calhoun*, 425-29.

[26] " Even in Tenn. in the neighborhood of the Hermitage itself, I am zealously and almost unanimously sustained ", he also wrote about this time.—*Corresp.*, 292.

of the Members of Congress were with him
against the President; that the opposition was
cracking and the most reflecting of the tariff-
men were not disposed to support Clay, for fear
of his going too far with protection; that the members from Kentucky had gone home resolved to
push the election against Clay, whose partisans
hated Jackson and Van Buren so much that, if
Clay should fail of support, they would unite upon
any man to put Jackson out—"even take him
(Calhoun) with nullification on his head"; and
that therefore it would be best for the South to
stand uncommitted on the Presidential question
and concentrate her strength in pushing the principles for which she had been of late contending.
He thought that the great interests of the North,
the South and the West—respectively manufactures and protection, free trade, and internal improvements and the distribution of the public
lands—could be reconciled. To avoid all question
of constitutionality, he would amend the Constitution to authorize internal improvements, and set
apart for them the income from the public lands.
By this system the channels of trade with the
West would make Charleston the great city of the
South. He hoped to prevail on the North to lower
the tariff to the revenue point by singling out
some of the most important articles and giving

them a liberal protection, and enhance their profits still further by lowering the duties on all or nearly all the other articles of necessary consumption. Thus might come reconciliation between the sections. If this plan should fail or matters should continue, "he looked upon disunion as inevitable. And he thought it best, for the system of plunder such as it was now was the most despicable of all possible forms of government." In the traffic of interests carried on, the North could beat us. "We being the payer and they the receiver, they could outbid us with the West and always would do it." "He then hinted pretty strongly that if things went right, he might be placed in nomination for the Presidency next fall. I told him candidly that such a step would be imprudent at this moment both at home and abroad, and should not be thought of at this time. He agreed with me. He said his object was to throw himself entirely upon the South and if possible to be more Southern if possible. In advancing our principles therefore, we should advance him in the only way in which he desired to be advanced." After drinking tea with Calhoun, later in the day, Hammond added that undoubtedly Calhoun's mind was deeply engaged on the subject of the Presidency, about which he was "quite feverish".

Calhoun's sudden change of attitude to agreement with Hammond and saying that his object was to throw himself entirely on the South and be more Southern, indicated that he still, as in 1828, was trying to lead the leaders,—to his nomination. To keep in touch with the nullification press, he wrote to Hammond, May 16, 1831: "The course which you and our papers generally take, I think the correct one. Be silent in a great measure as to myself, except defensively, where you think justice requires it, but speak freely of men and measures, as far as they bear on principles that we deem sacred." [27]   That he did not soon either regain the confidence of the leaders or give up his plans and expectations is clearly shown by his letter of June 16, 1831, to his intimate political friend Samuel D. Ingham of Pennsylvania, who was still Jackson's Secretary of the Treasury. The McDuffie dinner was described as "caused by the accidental visit of McDuffie"; it was "wholly unexpected", altogether "imprudent" and brought matters to a crisis [as Hamilton had planned it should] which Calhoun felt that he must meet "promptly and manfully". [28]

[27] *Corresp.*, 291.

[28] "I intended to wait for Mr. Crawford's movement on me [he added], so as to have the great advantage of acting on the defensive, but the occurrence to which I refer will not admit [of] the uncertainty and delay of his movement."—*Corresp.*, 294.

Duff Green—who after the Jackson-Calhoun quarrel had gone over to the ardent support of Calhoun, and his daughter later married Calhoun's son [29]—made it still clearer that Calhoun continued to be hopeful of success along the lines first described to Hammond. Green was acting as if he was Calhoun's political manager in trying to have Calhoun brought out as a Presidential candidate in Virginia and in several Northern States.[30] On June 11, 1831, Hamilton reported to Hammond the receipt of a letter from Green holding out the most alluring probabilities of Calhoun's success in obtaining the nomination for the Presidency and of the willingness of the manufacturers to compromise on the principle of Cal-

[29] 7 *Southern History Assn.*, 161.

[30] Green's correspondence about this with R. K. Crallé (and others in Va.), also a journalistic friend of Calhoun and many years later his literary executor, is quoted in " Calhoun and his Political Friends ", 7 *Southern History Association Publications*, 165 ff. Calhoun had presumably been in confidential relations with Green before leaving Washington in March, 1831, but perhaps was not for two or three months thereafter. In that letter of June 16th to Ingham, Calhoun significantly wrote: " I have received also two letters from Green. I am not surprised at his embarrassment and distress. * * * I am surprised to hear from him, that he has not received my letters to him. I have written, including that which goes today, four or five letters. Will you say so to him. So far from neglect, I will ever hold him in high estimation for his honest and disinterested course [in turning against Jackson], under the most trying circumstances."—*Corresp.*, 295.

houn's speech in 1816, and that to this Hamilton
had replied, that "in no shape lot or scot would
we be included in the arrangement, that we would
take no part in the presidential election and that
I was quite sure that Mr. C.'s prospects were as
hopeless as his ruin would be certain if he was
brought to give his countenance to such a compact"; that "we should go on and abate not one
jot of our zeal in the support of our principles,
which we would sacrifice to the elevation of no
man on earth. • • • I have no doubt he moves in
this matter with Calhoun's sanction. • • • I
enclosed Mr. Calhoun copies of Green's letters to
me and my letter in reply, in order that he might
see the whole ground".[31] This further showed
their distrust of Calhoun.

Yet Calhoun was confident that the favorable
attention he attracted on his way home from
Washington—"unanimous with the exception of
a few dependent editors and their immediate partisans"[32]—existed elsewhere. "I do not fear to
carry the whole South with me, acting as it
becomes my duty, which I will take care to do. I
never stood stronger. I have the strongest assur-
ance of a decided and successful support in Virginia, which in the present state of things is all

[31] 6 *Amer. Hist. Rev.*, 746-47; Meigs, 1 *Calhoun*, 429-30.
[32] *Corresp.*, 290.

important" • • •. At that time it was thought
that the Anti-Masons might turn the scales in the
next Presidential campaign, on account of their
supposed numbers in Pennsylvania and New
York, where Duff Green soon tried to exercise
much influence.[33] Calhoun added that he was not
only not a Mason, but was enough of an Anti-
Mason to believe that the institution was useless
and pernicious, although he did not doubt that
many good men in the society had a very different view of it.[34] In the letter to Ingham, he said
that, if he came out, he would state his "opinions
freely, but modestly, as by those of the Virginia
[Madison's long] Report, Kentucky Resolutions
and your [Pennsylvania] supreme court in the
case of Cobbett in '98; and will also state my
opinion on all of the connected points, particu-
larly that of our adjustment of the conflict. • • •
My friends must judge whether the position I may
take will be such as that they can prudently and
patriotically maintain. • • • In the meantime
silence is the best policy. Leave me to meet the
occasion." [35]

[33] 7 *Southern History Assn.*, 168, 169.

[34] To Van Deventer, May 25, 1831, *Corresp.*, 292-93.

[35] *Corresp.*, 294-95. In his correspondence Calhoun's punctua-
tion is so poor that it is often necessary to disregard it in order
to make his meaning clear.

After Hammond's and Hamilton's direct warnings, after the speeches of McDuffie and Hayne as the spokesmen of the radicals and after that nettling toast and the many persistent inquiries [36] Calhoun felt compelled to explain his views. This he did in a politic manner in a long public letter, called an "Address on the relation which the States and General Government bear to each other", dated Fort Hill, July 26, 1831,[37] It was a complaisant and artful rewriting of the "Exposition" to serve as his personal manifesto.[38] Virginia's support being vital to his ultimate success, stress was put on the Virginia Resolutions and

[36] The editor of the Pendleton, S. C. *Messenger*, in which Calhoun's "Address" was printed, said: "Public curiosity has been excited on the subject of Mr. Calhoun's opinions on this question, and we have observed for some months past, repeated calls through the papers, for an expression of them."—Quoted in Charleston *Courier*, Aug. 4, 1831. Aug. 5, 1831, Calhoun wrote: "There has been so much solicitude to know my sentiments" etc. that he had recently expressed them.—*Corresp.*, 296.

[37] 6 *Works*, 59-94.

[38] He affected modesty (*Ibid.*, 62); declared that he yielded to none in love of the Union (being "too national has, indeed, been considered by many, even of my friends, my greatest political fault"), in respect for the maxim that the majority should rule and in attachment to the Supreme Court. The purpose in each case was to make more palatable what he was about to say against the actual conditions. He was "anxious * * * to intrude as little as possible on the public attention" and, wishing to avoid the harshness of referring to the Northern and the Southern sections, as such, he substituted "the stronger" and "the weaker" sections.

Madison's Report, but he carefully avoided all reference to Madison, one of the most potent influences of the opposition; and he undertook to make it appear that the word Virginia employed, *interpose,* meant *veto, nullify,* although the word *null* had been withdrawn to preclude just that inference.[39]   The doctrine Calhoun was expounding was not that of Virginia but of the Kentucky Resolutions of 1799 and of Jefferson's draft—nullification. "This right of interposition, thus solemnly asserted by the State of Virginia, be it called what it may,— State-right, veto, nullification, or by any other name,—I conceive to be the fundamental principle of our system, resting on facts historically as certain as our revolution itself, and deductions as simple and demonstrative as that of any political or moral truth whatever; * * * I solemnly believe it to be the solid foundation of our system, and of the Union itself" * * *.[40]   Neither McDuffie nor Turnbull could have claimed more nor have made it seem half so harmless.

The gravamen of Calhoun's argument was on the tariff, and this he set forth with clearness, force and unusual moderation.   He manifested a statesmanlike temper in appealing for reduction

[39] See *ante,* p. 82.   [40] 6 *Works,* 61.

to a fair system of revenue, along economic lines, before excitement and anger should drive out reason and bring in violence. Had his method been constitutional, his firm stand in favor of reducing the tariff to a revenue basis by the time the public debt should be paid off, would have been entirely right; for the protectionists were planning to perpetuate the existing system by inaugurating a policy of national extravagance, and to seduce the South into supporting both protection and extravagance by distributing the surplus revenue— expected to be ten or twelve millions annually— among the States.[41] This would have created a most vicious circle. His aim was to represent nullification as the best shield against the protective tariff and other measures, actual or feared, alleged to be violative of the sovereignty of the States, and to make himself the exponent of the whole opposition.[42] Never doubtful of his own reasoning, he was doubly confident about this "Address":—"I know I am right. I have gone over the whole subject, with more care than I ever did any other; and I feel that I cannot be mistaken" * * *.[43]

[41] Corresp., 321; 6 Works, 81-83.

[42] He left out his "sentiments on the subject of internal improvement" because he thought it "not sufficiently connected with the subject in hand."—Corresp., 297.

[43] Corresp., 300.

"Mr. Calhoun's address was like a shock produced by the cold bath", Green informed Crallé, August 21, 1831. "His friends had been taught to believe that he was not a nullifier[,] little considering what the term implied. They expected him to denounce the doctrine because they supposed that he knew that such a measure would promote his popularity; and without knowing the man or examining his position they were shocked to find that he had not availed himself of the occasion to make himself popular." [44] A fortnight before the Anti-Masonic Convention in Baltimore, late in September, 1831, Green wrote: "The Anti-Masonic nomination is all that is wanting to put Clay out of the field and to elect Calhoun"; and again, on October 4th, that "but for the cry of Nullification Mr. Calhoun would have been nominated by the Anti-Masons". [45] Calhoun realized that he could not succeed without nullification. It should have been clear to him that he could not succeed with it. He knew his own ambition and South Carolina, but not the rest of the South and still less the North. Whatever he desired, seemed to him to be easily attainable; whatever he thought, seemed to him to be a fact. Otherwise he could hardly have expected to be able to run

[44] 7 *Southern History Ass'n.*, 167.
[45] 7 *Southern History Ass'n.*, 169.

with the hare of nullification and to hold with the hound of protection. His feverish hopes and Green's ardent plans were little better than political dreams.

In September, 1830—two years after the preparation of the "Exposition", and eight months after the Webster-Hayne debate, Calhoun had written privately to Virgil Maxcy:

" I consider the Tariff, but as the occasion, rather than the real cause of the present unhappy state of things. The truth can no longer be disguised, that the peculiar domestick institution of the Southern States, and the consequent direction, which that and her soil and climate have given to her industry, has placed them in regard to taxation and appropriations in opposite relations to the majority of the Union; against the danger of which, if there be no protective power in the reserved rights of the States, they must in the end be forced to rebel, or submit to have their permanent interests sacrificed, their domestick institutions subverted by Colonization and other schemes, and themselves and children reduced to wretchedness. Thus situated, the denial of the right of the State to interfere constitutionally in the last resort, more alarms the thinking, than all other causes * * *." [46]

Again in a "Report" on the general subject of nullification, which he prepared for the South Carolina committee on federal relations, about November, 1831,[47] he expressed the significant opin-

[46] 1 Meigs, 419.

[47] 6 *Works*, 94-123. Meigs (1 *Calhoun*, 437) says that this was not used.

ion that, although the existing relations between
South Carolina and the General Government had
grown out of the protective tariff, the committee
deemed that question "of vastly inferior importance to the great question to which it has given
rise, and which is now at issue in the controversy;
[i. e.] the right of a State to interpose, in the last
resort, in order to arrest an unconstitutional act
of the General Government, within its [the
State's] limits. This they conceived to be by far
the most important question which can be presented under our system * * *."[48] And in still
another exposition of nullification, called an "Address to the people of South Carolina," which he,
near the end of 1831, prepared for, but which was
not used by, the legislature, he gave this warning:
"As yet, the principle has been applied only to
the duties on imports * * *; but the same principle * * * may be applied to * * * any purpose
that the majority may think to be for the general
welfare;—to the Colonization Society, as well as
to cotton and woollen manufactures".[49] Thus, in
Calhoun's view, the real question was not the
tariff but how to thwart the power of a hostile majority that made possible not only such a tariff
but also an attack on slavery by using the money

48 6 *Calhoun Works*, 95.
49 6 *Works*, 131.

of the United States to aid colonization and emancipation.

In the hope of enlisting patriotism, the Nullifiers called a convention of their State-Rights and Free-Trade party in Charleston on February 22, 1832, the centennial of Washington's birth. Hamilton expected that it would "sketch the chart we are to steer by".[50] It, at least, intensified public feeling by advocating resistance and a more thorough propaganda.[51]

The Unionists continued to put forth strong arguments and ridicule, hoping to break the prestige of their opponents. Petigru's numerous racy witticisms helped to cheer his colleagues. As often happens in times of intense excitement, religious revivals flourished. Robert Barnwell, Robert Barnwell Smith (Rhett), Henry L. Pinckney and other Nullifiers became converts. Petigru likened their new faith to Mahomet's, which combined war and devotion.[52] And C. G. Memminger,

[50] 6 *Am. Hist. Rev.*, 748.

[51] Houston, 104, 105.

[52] "Barnwell Smith and Robert Barnwell are full of the Holy Ghost, and it is announced that Henry L. Pinckney will oppose Dr. Palmer for the church, if he does not oppose Colonel Drayton for Congress."—Carson, *Petigru*, 104, 114, 128. Dr. Cooper's expulsion from South Carolina College was at least aided by these new converts, who wished "to purify their party of poor old Cooper" and thus "wipe off the aspersion from the party

early in 1832, anonymously published a satire in Biblical form, called the "Book of Nullification", that merrily burlesqued the leading Nullifiers.[53] The agitation waxed hotter and the demand for resistance grew bolder as relief from Congress seemed hopeless.

The greedy protectionists must have controlled Congress or there would have been an honest effort to reform the tariff, for its evils were notorious. The law of July 14, 1832, did, indeed get

and from the State of being governed by infidel principles ".— Carson, *Petigru*, 128.

[53] The following is one of the best passages. Referring to James Hamilton, Jr.'s speech at Colleton, he said:—

"And he opened his mouth and said, ' Ye men of Colleton! lo, the people of the East, who are called Yankees, have smote your land with a scourge; they have despoiled you of your substance and put chains upon your members; they have robbed your fields of their increase, and 'the fox peeps forth from your ruined chateaux.'

" And the men of Colleton turned their eyes to the East and to the West, for they knew not the thing which is called a ' chateau '; they felt their arms for chains, but they were free.

" And they looked forth on the fields, but they were fresh with verdure, and the land was without scourge; and they marveled greatly at the words of James.

" But James called aloud on the name of George [McDuffie] the Prophet.

" And George answered in a voice like the rushing of many waters and said unto the people, ' Awake, stand up, O men of Colleton, who have drunk at the hands of the Yankees their cup of fury.'

" ' Verily, I say unto you, that although your fields are green and your hands free, yet desolation and destruction and famine

rid of most of the special "abominations" of that
of 1828, and the system of minimums had worked
so badly that even its expected beneficiaries called
for its abolition. But a duty of 50 per cent *ad
valorem* was put on woollen goods.[54] And, as a
rule, the duties that were abolished or lowered
were on articles that had been taxed for revenue,
whereas those that had been levied for protection
were but little changed.[55] The purpose was to
make the principle of protection less open to
attack and to give it permanency, to fortify protection without substantial relief to the South.
This was what the Nullifiers had foreseen,[56] and it

shall surely come upon you, for by the spirit of John [C. Calhoun],
the Conjuror, I swear that great and inconceivable are the
evils which the tariff of John of Quincy [President Adams] shall
bring to pass.'

" ' Wherefore, O men of Colleton, let not your hearts be faint,
but hearken to the words of James and wax stronger in the
faith—for lo! I will show unto you a hidden secret.'

" Then George waved his hand before the eyes of the men
of Colleton, and they beheld in the air a host of Yankees bearing
from the fields of the South ' forty of every hundred parts ' of
the increase thereof.

And he gave them to drink of certain liquor, which James
and his companions had procured from the kingdom beyond
the great waters, even from the land of Champagne, and they
waxed warm, and they felt the chains and the shackles whereof
James had spoken."—Capers, 572.

[54] Taussig, 103-105.

[55] Sumner, *Jackson*, 223.

[56] 6 *Amer. Hist. Rev.*, 748.

was very different from the modification of the revenue system that Jackson had forecast in his letter of June 14, 1831.

A day before the bill was signed, the two South Carolina Senators and six of the nine Representatives in Congress issued an appeal to the people of their State, giving a concise and fairly sober account of the steady growth of protectionism since 1816.[57] The tariff system, they said, virtually exempted those who imposed the taxes from all responsibility to those who paid them; it actually conferred on the majority bounties proportioned to the burthens it imposed on the proscribed minority. And they expressed "their solemn and deliberate conviction that the protecting system must now be regarded as the settled policy of the country, and that all hope of relief from Congress is irrecoverably gone".

The Charleston *Mercury,* no longer "sluggish" but full of Hamiltonian "fire", prophesied that "as surely as our next legislature meets, a convention will be called to *nullify the act,* and as surely as South Carolina *nullifies,* her position will be *supported by every other Southern State".*[58]

[57] 42 *Niles's,* 412-14, prints the text, but 1831 is erroneously given as the year.

[58] 42 *Niles's,* 403.

The first aim of this appeal and this prophecy was to help elect the two-thirds majority of the legislature required for calling a State convention. Warned by the Unionists, who were none the less resolute in the face of increasing difficulties, many persons still hesitated and asked: Is it, indeed, certain that if a convention is assembled it will not hastily attempt interposition? What ground is there for the belief that "to interpose" does not mean to resist, and that resistance will not precipitate violent revolution?

Mainly to clear up such lingering doubts, the commander-in-chief of the Nullifiers, Governor Hamilton, on the eve of another election, besought the oracle—for such Calhoun continued to be—to speak again. The response, in a long letter to Hamilton, on "State Interposition", dated August 28, 1832, is called Calhoun's masterpiece among his many expositions. Nearly all the old points were once more reviewed. He explained that although a State had a right to nullify and there was a corresponding obligation on the part of the General Government to acquiesce, unfortunately this obligation had never been recognized! [59] But he felt certain that a State would be victorious if it attempted to exercise this right, for nullifica-

[59] 6 *Works*, 160-61.

tion would be obligatory on its citizens. They could be punished for a violation of a Federal law only after conviction by trial by jury, which the Constitution guarantees. But the citizens and the courts of the State would have to maintain the State laws. And no appeal could be made to the Supreme Court, for no record of the trial could be obtained from the State court. In any case, the judgment of the State would meantime be pronounced and executed without responsibility being incurred by anyone. He also explained that force could not be used, because the contest would be a legal and constitutional contest,—legal and constitutional, although the purpose was to vitiate the clear intent of the Constitution! Then he urged that if nullification, like secession, placed the State in the relation of a foreign nation, it might be different; but nullification would not dissolve the bond, it would only repudiate the unwarranted act of the agent. Accordingly it was "in its nature peaceable, consistent with the federal relations of the State, and perfectly efficient, whether contested before the courts, or attempted to be resisted by force".[60] This was a positive promise of relief and success without any risks.

[60] 6 *Works,* 172.

In the "Exposition" of 1828 Calhoun had maintained that it would be absurd to seek relief by constitutional amendment.[61] At that time his chief aim was to have his theory, that state sovereignty made the General Government merely an agent, accepted as a fundamental principle of the Constitution. Then the right of nullification would logically follow and operate like a decision of the Supreme Court that a law or an exercised power was unconstitutional, dead. In fact, the purpose was to have a State's convention supersede the Supreme Court in judging constitutional questions concerning that State. By 1832 he believed that wide acceptance of his dogma had substantiated it for practical purposes. Gaining like recognition for the next step in his reasoning was then in order. As we know, the Constitution says that "the Congress, whenever two-thirds of both houses *shall deem it necessary*,[62] shall propose amendments to this Constitution, or, on the application of the legislatures of two-thirds of the several States, shall call a convention for proposing amendments." But Calhoun contended with more force than in previous expositions that whenever a State "interposed", nullified a law, "it would be the duty of the General Government [as in the

[61] *Ante* p. 45.
[62] Italics are not in the original.

case of a law declared unconstitutional by the
Supreme Court] to abandon the contested power,
or to apply to the States themselves, the source
of all political authority, for the power, in one
of the two modes prescribed in the Constitution.''
From that point forward, he would use what
partly resembled the constitutional method of
amendment, for that would require three-fourths
of the States to *undo nullification!* Yet, after thus
reversing the Constitutional method and making
stability dependent on a single State, he, with
benevolent condescension, said in substance: Let
us act in a perfectly constitutional manner. If
you ought to have the nullified power, you need
only to secure the coöperation of three-fourths of
the States to obtain it. All this is just and proper,
and to persons who know the facts and the Constitution and can reason calmly it is perfectly
clear; but, in the prejudice and the passion of the
time, perhaps we ought not to expect general
acceptance of our views.[63]

[63] The passage is so characteristic that it must be quoted:—
" If the views presented be correct, it follows that, on the
interposition of a State in favor of the reserved rights, it would
be the duty of the General Government to abandon the contested
power, or to apply to the States themselves, the source of all
political authority, for the power, in one of the two modes prescribed in the Constitution. If the case be a simple one, embracing a single power, and that in its nature easily adjusted, the

For Calhoun's purposes, this "masterpiece" was theoretically perfect. All that was lacking to make a practical success was to obtain recognition of nullification by the Federal Government. Then George S. Bryan's toast at the Unionist Fourth of July celebration would be realized—"Nullification: Anarchy reduced to system".[64]

This was near the climax of what James Ham-

more ready and appropriate mode would be an amendment in the ordinary form, on a proposition of two thirds of both Houses of Congress, to be ratified by three fourths of the States; but, on the contrary, should the derangement of the system be great, embracing many points difficult to adjust, the States ought to be convened in a general Convention—the most august of all assemblies—representing the united sovereignty of the confederated States, and having power and authority to correct every error, and to repair every dilapidation or injury, whether caused by time or accident, or the conflicting movements of the bodies which compose the system. * * *

" In the discussion, I have advanced nothing but on the authority of the Constitution itself, or that of recorded and unquestionable facts connected with the history of its origin and formation; and have made no deduction but such as rested on principles which I believe to be unquestionable; but it would be idle to expect, in the present state of the public mind, a favorable reception of the conclusions to which I have been carried. There are too many misconceptions to encounter—too many prejudices to combat—and, above all, too great a weight of interest to resist."—6 *Works*, 179-80.

[64] Capers, *Memminger*, 103. Less concisely, McDuffie, when a nationalist, said this in 1821: " The several independent sovereign States control the General Government! This is anarchy itself." And James Hamilton, Jr., then approved it.— Hunt, *Calhoun*, 77.

ilton, Jr., in his eulogy of Turnbull, called "five years of the most intense agitation and concussion of public mind" and the most powerfully contested canvass that had been waged since the era of the Revolution. At last, it looked as if enough fuel had been put on the fire—perhaps too much. Both the Unionists and the Nullifiers, too eager and too suspicious to restrict themselves to ordinary methods, employed bribery, kidnapped voters and kept them drunk and locked up until the election.[65] Several Unionists were struck with brickbats, antagonistic groups narrowly escaped street-fights; challenges were given and one or more serious duels occurred.[66]

All influences seemed to work for nullification. Many timid persons, snarled in sophistries and State pride, fancied that there was an insuperable magic about nullification that rendered it, as Calhoun had assured them, "peaceable, consistent with the federal relations of the State, and perfectly efficient, whether contested before the courts, or attempted to be resisted by force", and that consequently it would prevent secession and civil war. With his oracular dogmas Calhoun had beguiled credulous and imagina-

[65] Grayson, *Petigru*, 129; Carson, *Petigru*, 85; Boucher, *Nullification Controversy*, 157, 205-06.

[66] Carson, *Petigru*, 99-104.

tive South Carolinians into believing that he would lead them on a successful and heroic political adventure without real peril. Why longer hesitate? The combined influences caused an ample majority of radicals to be elected, although the popular vote was only about 23,000 to about 17,000. By a proclamation prepared in advance, Governor Hamilton summoned an extra session of the new legislature. It soon met and promptly called a State convention, by a vote of more than two to one in the senate and of nearly four to one in the house—31 to 13 and 96 to 25, respectively.

CHAPTER VIII

NULLIFICATION PROCLAIMED. — FINAL EFFORTS OF
THE UNIONISTS.—PRESIDENT JACKSON'S STAND

The nullification convention met in the State
capitol November 19, 1832, Governor Hamilton
presiding. Meantime Clay had been so emphatically defeated that his "American system"
seemed to be repudiated by a large majority of
the voters. Accordingly it appeared not to be
very dangerous to take the long-contemplated
step. The convention completed its work in six
consecutive days, November 19-24, for plans had
been well thought out. Hayne prepared the
lengthy report explaining the reason for the convention and the tasks before it.[1] Consolidation
was evidently considered the all-comprehensive
danger.[2] Judge William Harper drafted the ordi-

[1] Jervey, *Hayne*, 319.

[2] " We fearlessly appeal to all considerate men, whether it be in
the nature of things possible, to hold together such a Confederacy
as ours, by any means short of military despotism, after it has
degenerated into a CONSOLIDATED GOVERNMENT—that is to say,
after it shall come to be its established policy to exercise a
general legislative control over the interests and pursuits of the
whole American people.

" * * * No sooner had Congress assumed the power of building
up manufactures, by successive tariffs—calculated and intended
to drive men from agriculture and commerce, into more favored
pursuits—than internal improvements sprung at once into vigor-

nance of nullification. Turnbull, in the "Address
to the people of South Carolina", plausibly main-

ous existence. *Pensions* have been enlarged to an extent not
only before unknown in any civilized country, but they have been
established on such principles, as manifest the settled purpose
of bestowing the public treasure in gratuities, to particular
classes of persons and particular sections of country. *Roads
and canals* have been commenced, and surveys made in certain
quarters of the Union, on a scale of magnificence, which evinces
a like determination to distribute the public wealth into new and
favored channels; and it is in entire accordance, both with the
theory and practice of this new system, that the General Government should absorb all the authority of the States, and eventually
become the grand depository of the powers, and the general
guardian and distributer of the wealth of the whole Union. It
is known to all who have marked the course of our national
affairs, that Congress has undertaken to create a BANK, and
have [sic] already assumed jurisdiction over *science* and the *arts*,
over *education*, and *charities*, over *roads* and *canals*, and almost
every other subject, formerly considered as appertaining exclusively to the States, and that they claim and exercise an *unlimited
control* over the appropriation of the *public lands*, as well as of
the *public money*. On looking, indeed, to the legislation of the
last ten years, it is impossible to resist the conviction that a
fatal change has taken place in the whole policy and entire
operation of the Federal Government; that in every one of its
departments, it is both in theory and practice rapidly verging
towards consolidation—asserting judicial supremacy over the
sovereign States, extending EXECUTIVE PATRONAGE and influence to the remotest ramifications of society, and assuming
legislative control over every object of local concernment, thereby reducing the States to petty corporations, shorn of their
sovereignty, mere parts of one great whole, standing in the same
relation to the Union, as a county or parish to the State, of
which it is a subordinate part.

Such is the true character, and such the inevitable tendencies
of the AMERICAN SYSTEM." * * *—*Journals of the Conventions of
the People of S. C. held in 1832, 1833 and 1852*, 39-40.

tained that nullification was a constitutional right although not derived from the Constitution.[3] McDuffie wrote the address to the people of the other States.[4] The ordinance of nullification was adopted by a vote of 136 to 26.[5] It declared the tariff acts of 1828 and 1832 "null, void, and no law, nor binding upon this State, its officers or citizens." All officers of the State, except members of the legislature, and all jurors were required to take an oath to obey the ordinance and the laws made to give it effect; the enforcement

[3] "We claim it as a CONSTITUTIONAL right—not meaning, as some have imagined, that we *derive* the right from the Constitution, for derivative rights can only belong to the *functionaries* of the high contracting parties to the Constitution, but we claim to exercise it as one of the PARTIES to the compact, and as consistent with its letter, its genius and its spirit—it being distinctly understood at the time of ratifying the Constitution, that the exercise of all sovereign rights not agreed to be had conjointly, were to be exerted separately by the States. * * * Any exercise of a right in conformity with a Constitutional provision, we conceive to be a *Constitutional* right, whether it be founded on an express grant of the right, or be included in a general reservation of undefined power."—*Journals of Conventions* etc., 59.

[4] Stillé, *Poinsett*, 45-46; Jervey, *Hayne*, 319. Calhoun prepared a draft, only the first few pages of which McDuffie followed to any considerable extent, and this was with many variations in words and phrases.—6 *Calhoun's Works*, 193 ff. and *Journals of Conventions* etc., 68 ff.

[5] *Journals of Conventions* etc., 25-26, 49-51; 1 *S. C. Stats. at Large*, 329-33. Many of the important documents on nullification are printed in *Cong. Deb.*, 1832-33, Apdx., 154 ff.

of the payment of custom duties was forbidden; and the legislature was required to pass laws to give effect to this ordinance on and after February 1, 1833. In order to paralyze within the State the constitutional and exclusively national power of collecting the customs, appeal to the United States Supreme Court was prohibited in cases touching the authority of this ordinance or of laws to enforce it or the acts nullified. And if the General Government should attempt to use force against the State or in any way to coerce her or her citizens into obedience to the nullified laws, the people of the State would consider themselves absolved from all political connection with the people of the other States, and would proceed to organize an independent government. Thus the substance of Calhoun's theories, elaborating Jefferson's, was "peaceably" to make nullification a part of the organic law of the State.

Yet South Carolina was "willing to make a large offering to preserve the Union", said the Address to the States; "and with a distinct declaration that it is a concession on our part, we will consent that the same rate of duty may be imposed upon the protected articles that shall be imposed upon the unprotected, provided that no more revenue be raised than is necessary to meet the demands of the Government for constitutional purposes; and provided also, that a duty, substantially uniform, be imposed upon all foreign imports.'' Then with confidence, so characteristic of the radicals and which enabled them to believe that merely remote possibilities were virtual certainties, it was added: ''If South Carolina should be driven out of the Union, all the other planting States, and some of the Western States would follow by an almost absolute necessity.''[6] Audacity had become so habitual with the leaders that they felt themselves benevolent in advising the Federal Government that by accepting political impotency it could avoid both nullification and disunion.

Laws designed to make nullification effective and to prevent punishment for resistance to Federal authority were promptly passed. The governor was authorized to call out the militia to resist coercion, and to purchase ten thousand stands of arms and the necessary munitions of war.[7] The aim was to make enforcement appear so hopeless that it would not be attempted. The leaders manifested superior abilities and uncommon singleness of purpose for their undertakings.

[6] *Journals of Conventions*, etc., 76.

[7] The texts of the acts for replevin, test oaths and to carry the ordinance into effect are given in *Cong. Deb.*, 1832-33, Apdx., 177-81.

To buttress this merely South Carolina struc-
ture and to give a practical basis to the theory
that one State had a right to suspend a law of
Congress until three-fourths of the States declared the law constitutional, the South Carolina
legislature on December 18, 1832, resolved that it
was "expedient that a Convention of the States
be called as early as practicable to determine and
consider such questions of disputed power, as
have arisen between the States of the confederacy
and the General Government." [8] This resolution
was sent to the other States and to the South
Carolina delegation in Congress. It was not a
proposition for a real constitutional convention,
but it was a counterfeit presentment: it presup-
posed that unless three-fourths of the States in
convention approved of the tariff acts of 1828 and
1832, they must be treated as unconstitutional,
and that meantime the Federal Government was
bound not to attempt to enforce them in South
Carolina. This was no more warranted by the
Constitution than a popular referendum on a
treaty or a decision of the Supreme Court would
be. But Jefferson's theories had developed into
Calhoun's dogmas, which to the Nullifiers had
become an obsession.

[8] Ames, 176.

Meantime the Unionists had held to their course with exemplary courage and self-control, although waging a losing contest. Hoping to prevent the election of a two-thirds majority of the legislature favorable to calling a State convention, they had met at Columbia, in September, 1832, and Petigru in his most effective style had reported an address to the people, saying that the Unionists were as much opposed to the tariff as were the Nullifiers and were ready to coöperate with them for any constitutional purpose.[9] Delay and a convention of the Southern States to consider a redress of the grievances were also urged.[10]

[9] Here are some of his most pointed sentences:—

"The theory renders the Constitution a dead letter—and the practical enforcement of the doctrine is the beginning of Revolution. * * * It is monstrous to contend that the framers of the Constitution did not invest the general Government with power to execute their own laws, or that without such power a union can exist. * * * According to the theory of nullification any number of States, more than one fourth of the whole, may change the Constitution, * * * and this power of a minority to alter the Constitution is deduced from the express provision that it shall not be altered by a majority of less than three-fourths. * * * A construction which destroys the text and gives to words an effect directly opposite to their sense and meaning is too gross for argument. * * * It [nullification] is not merely an infraction of the Constitution, but a total abrogation of its authority. * * * But *nullification* in practice must produce a direct collision between the authorities of the States and those of the Union." —Carson, *Petigru*, 92-93.

[10] Carson, *Petigru*, 91-96, gives the text.

When the legislature, a few weeks later, called the
State convention, the Union members issued a
warning against nullification and summoned
Unionists to meet at the capital at the same time
as the State convention. After the ordinance of
nullification was passed they again convened at
Columbia, in December, 1832, and prepared a
remonstrance and protest, written by Petigru,
Poinsett and Memminger,[11] and presented it to
the legislature, as a final appeal against further
extreme action. Many counts in the indictment
were very sharp; that against the test oath was
thoroughly indignant. The Unionists also aroused
patriotism by organizing "Washington Societies"
and equiped themselves with arms so as to meet
nullification with physical force and to coöperate
with the General Government. But not one of
these well-planned enterprises was of much avail,
notwithstanding the liveliest aid on the part of
the Union press and of such orators as Drayton,
Poinsett, Huger and Grimké.[12]

President Jackson had not been a neutral ob-
server of what had been developing. Privately he
had early expressed his disapproval of the "South

[11] Carson, *Petigru*, 108.
[12] See 43 *Niles's* 87-88, 175, 291, 349, and Stillé, *Poinsett*, 46, 48,
76 ff., for different points mentioned in his paragraph.

Carolina doctrine". His first public utterance had been at the dinner in celebration of Jefferson's birthday, April 13, 1830, nearly fifteen months before the publication of the letter of June 14, 1831. Advocates of nullification had somehow obtained control of the arrangements and hoped, under cover of eulogy of Jefferson and praise of Virginia and Georgia for having championed state-rights, to make a start toward drawing the party leaders into apparent approval of vigorous resistance to the protective tariff. Then South Carolina could advance without much risk. At such political banquets it was then customary to offer prepared and volunteer toasts, as a means of eliciting opinions of the kind desired. Suspecting an unpatriotic purpose and wishing to thwart it at the earliest opportunity, Jackson, in conference with Van Buren, his Secretary of State, decided well in advance what he should do. Hayne, one of the principal speakers, lauded Jefferson and said that South Carolina's attitude was based on the principles that the old Republicans of Virginia had sustained and that Georgia had carried to victory in the controversy about the Indians. And three-fourths of the prepared toasts were favorable to state-rights. When the President was invited to give a toast, he proposed: "OUR FEDERAL UNION

—IT MUST BE PRESERVED!"[13]   The surprise, vigor
and patriotism of his sentiment occasioned intense applause. In turn, Vice-President Calhoun
responded with "The Union,—next to our Liberty most dear. May we all remember that it
can only be preserved by respecting the rights of
the States and distributing equally the benefit and
the burthen of the Union." His epigrammatic first
sentence would have been more effective if it had
stood alone.

Jackson's toast was a great disappointment to
the Nullifiers. But their natural resiliency soon
asserted itself when the thought occurred to them,
that the President that had allowed Georgia to
defy Federal authority would not be likely to
assert it against South Carolina. Not until the
publication of the letter of June 14, 1831, did they
fully realize that the impetuous "Old General"
was to oppose them. From the early autumn of

[13] Van Buren's *Autobiography*, which gives a vivid and detailed
account of the occasion (pp. 413-17), says: "General Hayne left
his seat and ran to the President to beg him to insert the word
'federal', so that the toast should read, 'OUR FEDERAL UNION—
IT MUST BE PRESERVED!' This was an ingenious suggestion as it
seemed to make the rebuke less pungent, although it really had no
such effect. The President cheerfully assented because in point
of fact the addition only made the toast what he had originally
designed it to be—he having rewritten it, in the bustle and
excitement of the occasion, on the back of the list of regular
toasts which had been laid before him, instead of using the copy
in his pocket, and having omitted that word inadventently."

1832 he was on the alert to make Federal representatives and resources at Charleston effective, and General Scott was sent there to take command. Not for a moment was Jackson in doubt about his obligations to enforce the laws and resist South Carolina's aims. From November 7th, twelve days before the convention assembled, he was in close correspondence with Joel R. Poinsett, giving positive assurances of sympathy with the Unionists and of determination to overcome and punish the Nullifiers.[14]

Jackson officially replied to South Carolina's nullification convention in his proclamation of

[14] Stillé, *Joel R. Poinsett,* 61 ff. Dec. 9, 1832: "The vain threats of resistence by those who have raised the standard of rebellion show their madness and folly. You may assure those patriots who cling to their country, and this Union, which alone secures our liberty and prosperity and happiness, that in forty days, I can have within the limits of South Carolina fifty thousand men, and in forty days more another fifty thousand. How impotent the threat of resistance with only a population of 250,000 whites and nearly that double [sic] in blacks, with our ships in the port, to aid in the execution of our laws! The wickedness, madness and folly of the leaders and the delusion of their followers, in the attempt to destroy themselves and our Union has not its parallel in the history of the world.—The Union will be preserved. The safety of the republic, the supreme law, which will be promptly obeyed by me."—*Ibid.,* 65. Jan. 16, 1833: "The first act of treason committed, unites to it, all those who have *aided* and *abetted in* the execution to [sic] the act— we will strike at the head and demolish the monster, Nullification and secession, at the threshold by the power of the law."— *Ibid.,* 66.

of December 10, 1832. This great state-paper was composed by Van Buren's successor, Edward Livingston, as was rumored and widely believed at the time and became known about thirty years later;[15] but Jackson's decision, rugged logic and ardent Unionism inspired and pervaded it. It was designed to be so clear and convincing that the people should free themselves from the sophistries of their leaders. In this it failed, but it blasted the theoretical foundation of nullification, in a manner that was wonderfully popular outside of South Carolina. The provincial conceits and State sentiments of the "unsafe guides" were contrasted with the national services and ideals of the South Carolina patriots of the Revolutionary period. Much more than Webster's reply to Hayne, which had prepared the way, this appeal of a Southern President in behalf of the glories of the Union made South Carolina, "my native State", as Jackson alleged,[16] appear to the rest of the country like a victim of self-delusions; and in no uncertain terms notice was given that the laws declared null and void must be obeyed. "Those who told you that you might peaceably prevent their execution, deceived you—they could

15 C. H. Hunt, *Edward Livingston* (1864), 371-73, 380-81. Ames, 173.

16 Stillé, *Poinsett*, 68.

not have been deceived themselves. • • • Their object is disunion; but be not deceived by names; disunion by armed force is treason." The message "created a monstrous sensation" in South Carolina and "put the Nullifiers into a roasting ferment", according to Petigru. To them it looked like "the black cockade Federalism of '98 revived, fearfully invigorated by its long sleep".[17]

The legislature retorted by resolving that each State had a right "for the preservation of its liberties or vital interests, to secede peaceably from the Union"; that "the primary and paramount allegiance of the citizens of this State, native or adopted, is of right due to this State"; that the State would "repel force by force, and, relying upon the blessing of God, will maintain its liberty at all hazards". And it requested Hayne, recently chosen governor, to warn the people against "the attempt of the President of the United States to seduce them from their allegiance" and to "exhort them to disregard his vain menaces".[18]

Hayne complied by sounding the alarm on account of the President's "dangerous and pernicious doctrines". One passage in his restatement of South Carolina's case said "that the States are as sovereign now as they were prior to the enter-

[17] James H. Hammond to Hayne, 6 *Am. Hist. Rev.*, 751.
[18] 1 *S. C. Stats. at Large* (1836), 356-58.

ing into the compact—that the Federal Constitution is a confederation in the nature of a treaty, or an alliance, by which so many sovereign States agreed to exercise their sovereign powers *conjointly* upon certain objects of external concern in which they are equally interested; such as WAR, PEACE, COMMERCE, Foreign Negotiation and Indian Trade; and upon all other subjects of civil government, they were to exercise their sovereignty separately." [19] He also maintained that "the only plausible objection" to the right to nullify was that it might be abused. He considered this danger "altogether imaginary", for "so long as our Union is felt as a blessing—and this will be just so long as the Federal Government shall confine its operation within the acknowledged limits of the charter—there will be no temptation for any State to interfere with the harmonious operation of the system." He further argued that the President had no right to use the military arm of the government to enforce the laws. The methods that the President contemplated employing were like those "by which the people have in every age been reduced to slavery", and South Carolina's

[19] *Ibid.* 361. This was borrowed almost verbatim from the Address to the People of S. C., written by Turnbull.—*Journals of Conventions*, 55.

struggle was similar to that with the mother country. Apparently with all the sincerity of men in a struggle for liberty against tyranny, he employed these grandiloquent sentences: "We will stand upon the soil of Carolina and maintain the sovereign authority of the State, or be buried beneath its ruins." "If our country must be enslaved, let her not be dishonored by her own sons!" "In such a sacred cause, South Carolina will feel that she is not struggling for her own, but the liberties of the Union, and the RIGHTS OF MAN, and she confidently trusts that the issue of this contest will be an example to free-men, and a lesson to rulers throughout the world."

With the regular miltia and the new volunteers, South Carolina expected soon to have twenty thousand armed men, ready to support and defend the policy of nullification. Almost a thousand Unionists were said to be no less ready to aid President Jackson in the enforcement of the United States laws. In some parts of the State nearly all voters seemed willing to fight on one side or the other.[20]   How different from the "more

[20] On Feb. 5, 1833, James H. Hammond attended a muster where the sentiment had previously been evenly divided, but now " every individual present volunteered." There was a company of volunteer veterans whose ages averaged 61, and five of the number were 80 years old. Many of them had fought through the Revolu-

perfect Union'' that the Constitution was designed to establish and from the prophesied fruits of nullification as a ''peaceful remedy''!

tion and most of them served in the War of 1812. They requested to be sent first into service. Thus under the influence of agitation, nullification and oratorical mustering " Everyone seemed ready to fight and all appear animated by a most thorough conviction that we are unconquerable."—6 *Am. Hist. Rev.*, 751; vii. 96.

CHAPTER IX

The Attitude of Other Southern States.—The Action of Congress.—Calhoun in the Senate.—Passage of the Compromise

Except in a few Southern States, anti-protection sentiment in most of the South had become more angry since the Harrisburg convention and the tariff of 1828.[1] But Kentucky and Louisiana, some of whose products the tariff had shielded from competition, were exceptions and had openly defended the policy of protection; Louisiana even agreed with Vermont that the tariff of 1828 was "constitutional, expedient, and harmless to the Southern States".[2] The Southern States, minus a few, had denounced the tariff as unconstitutional and injurious, while the Northern States and two Southern had defended it as constitutional and beneficial.[3] Dominant political opinion had followed the supposed economic interests.

[1] Ames, 152 ff.

[2] Ames, 162. The legislature of Pa. not unnaturally considered that the prosperity of the country was a demonstration of the wisdom of protecting manufactures, and deprecated any diminution of the tariff as impolitic and injudicious.—Ames, 163. S. C. later effectively retorted to the repeated claims that the tariff was just and that as a tax it was an equal one: "If this were so, how is it to be accounted for, that high duties are regarded in that quarter of the Union, not as a burden, but as a blessing?"— *Journals of Conventions* etc., 32. [3] Ames, 178.

143

Yet, notwithstanding their anti-tariff resolutions, not one of the other Southern States would support South Carolina in nullification. Mississippi called it "a heresy fatal to the existence of the Union"; North Carolina pronounced it "revolutionary in its character, subversive of the Constitution of the United States and [a doctrine that] leads to a dissolution of the Union." Alabama characterized it as "unsound in theory and dangerous in practice" and "leading in its consequences to anarchy and civil discord." Even Georgia, which had previously and successfully resorted to virtual nullification, said: "We abhor the doctrine of nullification as neither a peaceful nor a constitutional remedy but, on the contrary, as tending to civil commotion and disunion."[4] The Virginia legislature declared that, while still regarding the doctrines of state-sovereignty and state-rights as set forth in the resolutions of 1798 and the report of 1799 as the true interpretation of the Constitution, it (the legislature) did not consider them as sanctioning South Carolina's proceedings; it entreated South Carolina to repeal the ordinance and Congress to reduce the tariff, and sent a commissioner to South Carolina to

---

[4] Ames, 180; See *State Papers on Nullification*, 101 ff., for the attitudes of the different States toward S. C. and the Federal Government. Ames, 178 ff., quotes many of them.

facilitate a peaceful settlement.[5]   And Kentucky, the State that in 1799 had been most extreme in theoretical nullification, was surpassed by none in antagonism to South Carolina's acts and doctrines. A long report of a committee of the Kentucky house of representatives and resolutions passed by the legislature stoutly controverted not only the main contentions of the Nullifiers, but were also a virtual repudiation of Kentucky's theories of 1798 and 1799.[6]

[5] Ames, 186-88.

[6] Acts of Ky., 1832-33, 309-16. These sentences from the report show how the ordinance violates the Constitution of the U. S.:

" That instrument [the Constitution] declares that the judicial power therein delegated, shall extend to all cases in law and equity arising under the Constitution, the laws of the United States and treaties made, or which shall be made, under their authority. The Ordinance forbids an appeal to the Supreme Court of the United States, in any case in law or equity, in which the acts of Congress of the 19th of May, 1828, and the 14th of July, 1832, are, or shall be drawn in question.

" The Constitution proclaims itself, and the laws of the United States made in pursuance thereof, and all the treaties made or which shall be made under the authority of the United States, to be the supreme law of the land, and the judges of every state shall be bound thereby, anything in the Constitution or laws of any state to the contrary notwithstanding. The Ordinance declares itself paramount and binding upon the citizens of South Carolina, and makes all officers, judicial and others, within the state, swear to observe and execute it.

" The Constitution provides that all duties, imposts and excises, shall be uniform throughout the United States. The Ordinance declares that no duties shall be collected within the limits of Carolina, under the existing revenue laws of the union, although

The resemblance between South Carolina's nullification and the Kentucky and the Virginia resolutions was much less marked than the unanimity
with which they had all been disapproved by other
States. Yet with profound self-reliance South
Carolina replied to the critical Southern States,
which had previously expressed quite different
opinions: "It is within the providence of God
that great truths should be independent of the
human agents that promulgate them. Once announced, they become the subjects and property
of reason to all men and in all time to come." [7]
And the Nullifiers acted as if South Carolina was
the chief sufferer from the tariff (although it was
still more injurious to Virginia) and the only
State fit to lead opposition to it.

they are in force every where else throughout the United States.

"The Constitution gives to Congress the power to provide for
calling forth the militia of the union to execute the laws, suppress insurrections, and repel invasions. The Ordinance declares
that if Congress attempts to execute her [i.e. U. S.] laws by force,
South Carolina will organize a separate government, and maintain
her Ordinance at all hazards."—*Ibid.*, 311-12.

[7] *Journals of the Conventions, 1832-52*, 114. The nullification
convention's "Address to the People of South Carolina", as originally passed, contained the words "with a full confidence that
other divisions of the Confederacy will nobly follow and sustain
us". After a reconsideration was carried, Turnbull's proposal to
strike out these words was agreed to without opposition. While
hoping for such aid and comfort, South Carolina, he said, wished
to be understood as relying on herself alone.—*Ibid.*, 26.

If *after* nullification, Southern States had par-
ticipated in the kind of a convention that South
Carolina had proposed—a convention that would
necessarily have supported nullification unless a
three-fourths majority of it declared the protective tariff constitutional, which was wholly im-
probable—they would have walked open-eyed into
Calhoun's obvious trap. It was because he had
deceived himself into believing that they would do
so, that he was so confident that nullification would
be successful and peaceable. Not one of them had
the slightest notion of thus aiding South Carolina
in nullification, which was thoroughly disapproved of. Georgia desired a convention of Southern States, and Alabama recommended calling a
regular constitutional convention to consider
amendments and alterations, but neither of these
was in line with the wishes of the Nullifiers.[8]

Why had not South Carolina first tried to assemble a convention of Southern States to protest
against the tariff, and postponed nullification until
joint and constitutional methods had been thoroughly tried? Let Calhoun answer. "In fact, it may
well admit of doubt, whether it would be desirable
to have a convention of the States till some one
of them had interposed", he wrote December 25,

[8] Ames, 179-82.

1831, about eleven months before actual nullification, "as it is only by such action that a necessity of acting on the subject could be imposed on the other States, and without such necessity, nothing could be done".[9] Thus, by a revolutionary act, the expectation was either to gain a peaceable victory for nullification through failure of the General Government to resist it, or, if the General Government should attempt coercion, to enlist, on the basis of maintaining state-rights, the military aid of other Southern States, which would be likely to entail civil war and disunion.[10] Again and again the agitators and the ever-confident

[9] *Corresp.*, 306. He had about reached this conclusion nearly a year earlier.—*Ibid.*, 281. On Oct. 8, 1832, the day of the South Carolina election, when Calhoun was sure that a State convention would nullify the tariff, he wrote: " The end aimed at will be a General Convention of all the States, in order to adjust all constitutional differences and thus restore general harmony."— 1 Meigs, 447. This was not to be the kind of a convention the Constitution provides for, but the trap-convention that Calhoun designed and first suggested in the " Exposition " and that S. C. finally proposed. Turnbull also said: " Till some one Southern State tenders to the Federal Government an issue, it will continue to have its 'appetite increased by what it feeds on.' "— *Journals of Conventions*, 66.

[10] It was assumed that Va. and N. C. would forbid Federal troops to cross their borders.—Hamilton in 1828, 35 *Niles's*, 202, 208. Henry A. Wise of Va. grandiloquently said in Congress in 1841, that he had opposed nullification and was a Union man and for peace; but " if war had begun, every Union man of Va. would have been a Southern man. No standing army would ever have crossed her ancient lines, to do battle against a sovereign State,

Calhoun had prophesied that virtually the whole South would support South Carolina in nullification. They were so self-centered that it did not occur to them that public men in other States might have special plans of their own and not relish being made victims of such a headlong scheme.

It was not strange that Congress felt somewhat confused for several weeks after it met in December, 1832. Clay, who had been so proud of his once triumphant "American system", had been able to get but a little more than one-sixth (49 out of 288) of the electoral votes for the Presidency. Devotion to a policy that administers such a defeat to its champions forms no part of the patriotism that obtains on Capitol hill. Jackson, never an enthusiast for protection, felt safe in recommending, in his annual message, that the tariff should be reduced to a revenue basis, with certain reasonable exceptions. He had several times publicly indicated that he would favor a proper reduction of the tariff, but South Carolina would not wait. One reason was that Jackson had also publicly favored the distribution of the surplus revenue, which the Nullifiers considered more objectionable

without first fighting her sons of every faith at every pass where volunteers could have made a stand " etc.—Wise's *Henry A. Wise*, 39.

than the worst of tariffs. Before the end of December, Verplanck of New York reported a bill in the House designed to do away with most of the protective tariff. It had the approval of the Administration, and went far in the direction of South Carolina's demands.

Jackson had kept in close touch with the Unionists. His indignation at the "madness and folly" of the "nullies" and his determination to enforce the laws had not lessened. His message of January 16, 1833, asked Congress to authorize him to change or abolish certain ports of entry in South Carolina and to use the land and naval forces to execute the customs laws. This message was referred to the judiciary committee of each house.

Only five days later, January 21st, there was reported in the Senate the revenue collection bill, the "force bill"; the Nullifiers called it the "bloody bill" and the "Bill of Blood". Its aim was to give the Federal Government complete and summary jurisdiction of all cases arising under the custom laws and entirely to defeat South Carolina's efforts to secure exclusive control of the situation or compel the Federal Government to assume a violent aggressive.[11]

Also on January 21, 1833, eleven days before

[11] The text is given in *Cong. Deb.*, 1832-33, 244-46. Prof. Burgess (*The Middle Period*, 233-34) gives a good summary of it.

the ordinance of nullification was to go into effect, February 1st, a large meeting of Nullifiers, mostly citizens of Charleston, virtually suspended the ordinance pending Congressional action on the tariff, so as to avoid a collision and to facilitate a satisfactory adjustment. Both Virginia and Alabama, instead of giving aid and comfort, had recommended a suspension, but they could hardly have supposed that it would be effected by such a usurpation—an unauthorized meeting changing the date as to when a decree of a sovereign State convention should be operative.[12] The irregularity was concealed in violent resolutions and solemn resolves as to what would be done in case expectations should be disappointed. And Hamilton said that if the President's request for power to coërce South Carolina should be granted, he would forthwith reassemble the State convention and submit the question of secession.[13] This meeting also made initial plans for establishing a free-trade importing company by which all foreign merchandise consumed by South Carolinians should be "imported free from the odious and unconstitutional tribute which we have hitherto

[12] A few days later Hayne referred to the incident by saying that "public opinion has already suspended the Ordinance."— 7 *Am. Hist. Rev.*, 94.

[13] Charleston *Mercury*, Jan. 23, 1833.

paid." [14]   But, in any case, the Federal officers were determined to collect the customs as if there had been no ordinance of nullification.

The report of the judiciary committee of the House, February 8, 1833, expressed the opinion that the passage of the Verplanck bill would "tend more effectually to allay the excited feeling of the South, to avert the crisis with which we are threatened, and to restore harmony to our once happy Union, than any provisions which can be adopted for the removal of our custom-houses, clothing the courts with additional powers, or invasion by fleets and armies." [15]   But such a bill, without some kind of a force bill, could not have passed both houses.

The respective personal feelings of Jackson, Webster and Clay, and the peculiar circumstances of each, had much influence on the outcome.   Jackson, because his indignation and fighting spirit were fully aroused, cared most about having a real force bill, and perhaps he would not have objected if it had been a bit "bloody".   Next to a clear and prompt assertion of the authority of the Federal Government, he desired a low tariff.   Webster had made himself the intellectual exponent of constitutional nationalism.   He was entitled to feel the keenest personal

---

[14] 43 *Niles's*, 381.
[15] *Cong. Deb.*, 1832-33, Apdx., 201.

and patriotic interest in seeing his doctrines illustrated by a vigorous execution of the laws.[16] And this would keep attention on nullification and be least likely to disturb protection.

Clay surprised the Senate, February 12, 1833, by bringing in a tariff bill. He wished to save protection, the sudden abolition of which, he said with facile exaggeration, would cause mischief, to which history could produce no parallel. "The repeal of the Edict of Nantes itself was nothing in comparison with it"![17] His chief proposition in what became known as the compromise tariff was gradually to reduce the duty to 20 per cent *ad valorem,* by 1842. The free list was to be enlarged and no more revenue was to be raised than would be necessary for the economical support of the Government.[18] This slow reduction, with a substantial remnant of protection would prevent a

[16] "I think the people of the United States demand of us, who are intrusted with the Government, to maintain that Government; to be just, and fear not; to make all and suitable provisions for the execution of the laws, and to sustain the Union and the Constitution against whatsoever may endanger them. For one, I obey this public voice; I comply with this demand of the people. I support the Administration in measures which I believe to be necessary; and, while pursuing this course, I look unhesitatingly, and with the utmost confidence, for the approbation of the country."—*Cong. Deb.*, 1832-33, 411.

[17] *Cong. Deb.*, 1832-33, 462.

[18] *Cong. Deb.*, 1832-33, 482, gives the text of the bill.

serious shock. When reminded that, according to
the Constitution, a bill for raising the revenue
must originate in the House, he replied that this
"was not a bill to raise the duties, but to reduce
them"![19] He was allowed to introduce his bill. In
his gracefully meandering, half-equivocal style, he
let it appear that, although he considered South
Carolina entirely wrong as to nullification, the
recent assurances that her aims were peaceable
and not toward disunion, had led him to believe
that the passage of his compromise would suffice,
without the force bill, to restore her obedience.
He was more hopeful of coöperating with his
enemy, Calhoun, and the Nullifiers than with his
recently successful antagonist, Jackson, and the
vigorous nationalists, and he acted accordingly.

Meantime Prometheus had been unbound.
Shortly after Hayne withdrew from the Senate
to become governor, Calhoun resigned the Vice-
Presidency and, in December, 1832, succeeded him
as South Carolina's spokesman in Washington.
Duff Green had foretold this the previous July.[20]
Habitually a mild-mannered man, especially in
comparison with his fellow-Nullifiers, Calhoun

---

[19] *Cong. Deb.*, 1832-33, 477.
[20] 7 *Southern History Association*, 277.

realized the importance of moderation.[21]   When
he announced himself as being in a compromising
mood and ready, with slight misgivings, to support Clay, there was such "tumultuous approbation in the galleries" that they were, at first,
ordered to be cleared.[22]   But moderation and self-
control were not easy after his false prophecies of
sure and peaceable success of nullification had
wheedled South Carolina to the verge of civil war
and had made him the object of almost national
reprobation instead of admiration.   And it must
have been anything but soothing to know that it
was popularly believed that the President had
threatened to hang him.   Considering Jackson's
summary execution of Ambrister and Arbuthnot
in Florida—an incident that had been the occasion
of a very bitter quarrel between Jackson and
Calhoun—almost any violence on the part of the
President seemed not impossible.   Calhoun was
obviously much excited and he so extravagantly

[21] Jan. 10, 1833, Calhoun wrote from Washington: "Let our
people go on; be firm and prudent; give no pretext for force, and
I feel confident of a peaceable and glorious triumph of our cause
and the State."—*Corresp.*, 323.

[22] *Cong. Deb.*, 1832-33, 478.   Benton, many years later, plausibly
alleged that Clay and Calhoun were so ready to meet and to favor
a compromise and try to put the tariff out of politics, because
each had learned, in quite different ways—one by favoring and
the other by opposing the tariff—that it was an obstacle to advancement.—1 *Thirty Years' View*, 314.

criticised Jackson's message of January 16th that he soon felt compelled to apologize.[23]

The day after the revenue collection bill, the "force bill", was reported in the Senate, Calhoun introduced three resolutions asserting that the Constitution is a *compact;* that certain definite powers were *delegated* to the General Government; and that therefore there is *no nation* with any sovereignty, but that the States retained all the sovereignty and the allegiance of their respective citizens, and, consequently, each State had a right to judge both as to the powers delegated and those reserved.[24] Accordingly any-

[23] "It was stated by the Chief Magistrate, in substance, that the movements made by the State of S. C. were of a character hostile to the Union. * * * There was not a State in the Union less disposed than S. C. to put herself in such attitude of hostility." S. C. "entered the confederacy with the understanding that a State, in the last resort, has a right to judge of the expediency of resistance to oppression, or secession from the Union. And for so doing it is that we are threatened to have our throats cut, and those of our wifes and children. No—I go too far. I did not intend to use language so strong. The Chief Magistrate had not yet recommended so desperate a remedy. * * * But depart from these principles [of 1798], and in the course of ten years we shall degenerate into a military despotism. The cry had been raised, 'The Union is in danger'. He knew of no other danger but that of military despotism. He would proclaim it on this floor, that this was the greatest danger with which it was menaced—a danger the greatest which any country had to apprehend."—*Cong. Deb.*, 1832-33, 100, 103.

[24] *Cong. Deb.*, 1832-33, 191-92, and 2 *Calhoun's Works*, 262-63, give the text of the resolutions.

thing like the force bill must "tend directly and inevitably to subvert the sovereignty of the States, to destroy the federal character of the Union, and to rear on its ruins a consolidated government, without constitutional check or limitation, and which must necessarily terminate in the loss of liberty itself." He made no pretense of false modesty; as usual, he was confident that no one could resist his facts and reasoning.[25] His aim was to formulate a defense of South Carolina, using these resolutions as bases, and compel opponents to meet him on this chosen ground, which, if he could defend it, he frankly said, "must be a complete bar to the bill":[26] His sheer reasoning was to outlaw the bill in advance!

That betokened his bold self-appreciation and his depreciation of facts and of the resources of opponents. Contemporaries were wont to regale themselves by repeating stories, perhaps fabrications, illustrating this trait in the humorless Nullifier. According to one story, Calhoun at a

[25] " He had drawn them [the resolutions] with great care—with a scrupulous regard to the truth of every assertion they contained, which, he believed, no one who valued his character for candor could contradict, and that no impartial jury in christendom could, on an issue, refuse to render a verdict in their favor; and he had been equally scrupulous in making no deductions but what were sustained by the closest and most demonstrative reasoning."— *Cong. Deb.*, 1832-33, 187.

[26] *Cong. Deb.*, 1832-33, 238.

dinner-party in Washington undertook to instruct an English sea-captain about the trade-winds. The untraveled South Carolinian argued cogently and, of course, confidently. The captain finally remarked that he had often crossed the equator but his observations did not sustain Calhoun's theory. Yet the company, convinced by Calhoun's argument, were surprised that the captain's experience did not agree with it.[27]

Grundy of Tennessee countered Calhoun's resolutions by a series of his own, declaring that certain powers were wholly transferred from the State authorities to the General Government; that one of these was to levy duties on importations; that an attempt on the part of a State to annul an act of Congress, passed upon any subject exclusively confided by the Constitution to Congress, is an encroachment on the rights of the General Government; and that any attempts to obstruct such acts are not warranted by the Constitution and are dangerous to the political insti-

[27] At another time, Calhoun, who had never been abroad, was reported to have argued with Francis Lieber that the Southern slave was better off than mechanics in Europe, although the learned professor of history in South Carolina College was born and educated in Germany, in early manhood had spent several years in three or four other European countries, had edited the *Encyclopaedia Americana* and had published a book about the United States.

tutions of the country.[28] Clayton of Delaware presented thoroughly national resolutions, which went far beyond Grundy's.[29] And Webster's fine sarcasm must have been very discomforting:— In announcing that no one could deny his propositions the Senator from South Carolina had taken very bold ground, in fact, had declared his own infallibility. Although "The author of Hudibras made his hero see truth," Webster did not "pretend to have this personal acquaintance with truth; but, if to a mind as humble as his, the features of truth were ever exhibited, he was not able to identify them in the propositions of the gentleman from South Carolina." And he gave notice that Calhoun's indisputable facts were denied and would be taken issue with at the earliest opportunity.[30] Moreover, the Senate decided that Calhoun's resolutions, not being more important than the revenue collection bill, should wait.

Instead of conquering the Senate by his reasoning, Calhoun was soon busy offering plausible explanations for South Carolina and for himself. He pleaded that they were much more sinned against than sinning; that South Carolina had not acted precipitately, but the sister States tardily!

[28] *Cong. Deb.*, 1832-33, 192-93.
[29] *Cong. Deb.*, 1832-33, 231.
[30] *Cong. Deb.*, 1832-33, 241.

And in other ways he manifested his political astigmatism, his inability to ''see truth''.[31]

Since Calhoun's authorship of the ''Exposition'' of 1828 was first suspected in Washington,

[31] Frequent remarks after Jan. 28, 1833, and parts of his speech of Feb. 15th were largely of this character. When Grundy asked if S. C. had not legislated the United States out of the limits of the State, Calhoun answered: "No! not in the slightest degree. The State of South Carolina had done nothing more than to resort to the exercise of her delegated powers, for the purpose of preserving her reserved rights. * * * And after she had done this, up rose the monstrous giant of the United States, with his hundred arms, and, stepping forward, declared that he would put down that resistance by the interposition of his superior strength."—*Cong. Deb.*, 1832-33, 240.

"Never was there a political discussion carried on with greater activity, and which appealed more directly to the intelligence of the community" (2 *Calhoun's Works*, 214) than the nullification agitation in S. C. "No community, from the legislature to the plowman, were ever better instructed in their rights; and the resistance on which the State has resolved, is the result of mature reflection, accompanied with a deep conviction that their rights have been violated, and that the means of redress which they have adopted are consistent with the principles of the constitution."—2 *Calhoun's Works*, 215. * * * "the State was compelled to choose between absolute acquiescence in a ruinous system of oppression, or a resort to her reserved powers—powers of which she alone was the rightful judge, and which only, in this momentous juncture, could save her. She determined on the latter."

"So far from deserving the denunciation which has been leveled against it [the test oath], I view this provision of the ordinance as but the natural result of the doctrines entertained by the State, and the position which she occupies."—2 *Calhoun's Works*, 220.

"Whatever impedes the course of avarice and ambition, will ever be denounced as rash and precipitate; and had South Carolina delayed her resistance fifty instead of twelve years, she would

Webster had doubtless been looking forward to a debate with him. Benton, who was exceptionally well informed, "knew that Mr. Webster was speaking *at* him [Calhoun] in all that he said to Mr. Hayne." [32]   And Webster's sarcastic retort to Calhoun indicated eagerness for an encounter. The real debate between them was opened by Webster on February 16, 1833, for Calhoun's long speech of the previous day had not been directed

have heard from the same quarters the same language; but it is really surprising, that those who are suffering in common with herself, and who have complained equally loud of their grievances; who have pronounced the very acts which she has asserted within *her* limits to be oppressive, unconstitutional and ruinous, after so long a struggle—a struggle longer than that which preceded the separation of the States from the mother-country—longer than the period of the Trojan war,—should now complain of precipitancy! No, it is not Carolina which has acted precipitately; but her sister States, who have suffered in common with her, have acted tardily."—2 *Works*, 223.

Senator Grundy had called the force bill a " measure of peace." " Yes ", exclaimed Calhoun, " such peace as the wolf gives to the lamb—the kite to the dove!   Such peace as Russia gives to Poland, or death to its victim!   A peace, by extinguishing the political existence of the State, by awing her into an abandonment of the exercise of every power which constitutes her a sovereign community.   It is to South Carolina a question of self-preservation; and I proclaim it, that, should this bill pass, and an attempt be made to enforce it, it will be resisted at every hazard —even that of death itself.   Death is not the greatest calamity: there are others still more terrible to the free and the brave, and among them may be placed the loss of liberty and honor."— 2 *Works*, 229.

[32] Benton, 1 *Thirty Years' View*, 142.

at Webster. But Jackson with characteristic prejudice, wrote, February 17th, nine days before Calhoun's actual reply, that Webster was reported to have "demolished him" and "handled him as a child".[33] Calhoun's reply and Webster's rejoinder were made on February 26th. The strongest legal and historical reasoning was demanded, without any of the dash or tactics of the reply to Hayne, to whom Calhoun was much superior, except in eloquence and nimble wit. This debate was tense and very able; but each contestant, lawyerlike, made extreme and *ex parte* claims—Webster of nationalism and Calhoun of state-sovereignty—and thereby rendered himself vulnerable, because his argument ignored the mixed, complicated and sometimes paradoxical features of the Constitution. Each successfully refuted the other, while remaining fundamentally wrong on a main point. This would have been impossible if they had started with the realities as described by the wise and lucid Madison.[34] As a debater on his own

[33] Stillé, *Poinsett,* 71.

[34] Of Madison's many concise expositions of sovereignty, the following, written to Webster in acknowledgment of the receipt of his speech in this debate, seems to be the best:

"It is fortunate when disputed theories can be decided by undisputed facts. And here the undisputed fact is, that the Constitution was made by the people, but as imbodied into the several States, who were parties to it and therefore made by the

ground—on his false premises—Calhoun had no superior in logic and force. With intense concentration he marshaled his generalizations, selected certain facts and concealed others in misleading terms, so as to drive all but irresistibly to his conclusions. With apparent ease he could reason to any desired result, and it was very difficult to detect and refute his fallacies. Many a person unconvinced, yet unable to refute him, must have felt like paraphrasing Sir Robert Walpole's cynical remark about history by saying: Anything but your reasoning, for that must lead to what is unreasonable.[35]

As a direct exposition of the Constitution Webster's effort was superior to his ever-famous

States in their highest authoritative capacity. They might, by the same authority and by the same process have converted the Confederacy into a mere league or treaty; or continued it with enlarged or abridged powers; or have imbodied the people of their respective States into one people, nation or sovereignty; or as they did by a mixed form make them one people, nation, or sovereignty, for certain purposes, and not so for others."—9 *Madison's Writings* (Hunt), 604n.

[35] In this debate Senator John Forsyth of Georgia was so uncomplimentary as to say: " Much ingenuity had been called forth in support of nullification; but mystify it as they pleased, they could not stand the test of argument. The doctrine was preposterous; it was a mere web of sophism and casuistry. And the arguments in its favor, if analyzed, and put through the alembic, would result in the double distilled essence of nonsense."—Benton, 12 *Abridgment* etc., 111.

"Reply" of 1830, but, lacking surprises and picturesqueness, it was much less appreciated then and is much less famous now. Instead of attempting something like his immortal apostrophe to the Union, he concluded his brief rejoinder with these words of practical wisdom:—"Mr. President, turn this question over, and present it as we will—argue upon it as we may—exhaust upon it all the fountains of metaphysics—stretch over it all the meshes of logical or political subtlety—it still comes to this: Shall we have a General Government? shall we continue the union of the States under a *Government* instead of a *league?* This is the upshot of the whole matter; because, if we are to have a Government, that Government must act like other Governments, by majorities; it must have this power, like other Governments, of enforcing its own laws, and its own decisions; clothed with authority by the people, and always responsible to the people; it must be able to hold on its course, unchecked by external interposition. According to the gentleman's view of the matter, the constitution is a league; according to mine, it is a regular popular Government. This vital and all-important question the people will decide, and, in deciding it, they will determine whether by ratifying the present CONSTITUTION AND FRAME OF

GOVERNMENT they meant to do nothing more than to amend the articles of the old confederation.'' [36]

Notwithstanding Calhoun's numerous protests, the ''force bill'' had passed the Senate, February 20, 1833, by a vote of 32 to 1, out of a total of 48 members. Calhoun had asked to have the vote postponed from that night until the next morning because some Senators had to go home. When this request was denied, he and others withdrew, leaving only John Tyler of Virginia to vote against the bill.[37]

To hasten matters and to avoid the constitutional objection to the Senate leading with Clay's revenue bill, a Kentucky Representative, doubtless at Clay's request, moved the substitution of the Clay bill for that of Verplanck. The substitute was passed by the House on February 26th [38] and was at once sent to the Senate. There the original Senate copy of Clay's bill was laid on the table, and the House substitute was passed, March 1st, by a vote of 29 to 16 — Calhoun voting for it, Webster and Benton against it.[39] The father of the ''American system'' and the father of nullification as a means of overthrowing

[36] *Cong. Deb.*, 1832-33, 777.   [37] *Cong. Deb.*, 1832-33, 687-88.
[38] By a vote of 119 to 85.—*Cong. Deb.*, 1832-33, 1810-11.
[39] *Cong. Deb.*, 1832-33, 809.

that system had met and found a way to coöperate; the Southern and more than half of the Western votes in the House favored the compromise. South Carolina's avoidance of putting nullification to a positive test had mollified many nationalists, who were ready to favor a liberal reduction of the tariff on condition that the "force bill" should be passed first, to show the Government's power. Clay balanced, but foretold the outcome, by saying that the two bills should go forth together, "as well to show that the laws must be executed, as that there was a disposition to make concessions".[40]

Just after the House had passed the "force bill," also on March 1st,[41] McDuffie rose, as he said, "to perform a solemn duty": The House was about to destroy the rights of the States— was about to bury the Constitution. He wished to write its epitaph. He desired the title of this bill to be "An act to subvert the sovereignty of the States of this Union, to establish a consolidated government without limitation of powers, and to make the civil subordinate to the military power". This was equally theatrical and futile: his efforts were quickly defeated by a vote of nearly five to one.[42]

[40] *Cong. Deb.*, 1832-33, 807.
[41] By a vote of 149 to 48.—*Cong. Deb.*, 1832-33, 1903.
[42] *Cong. Deb.*, 1832-33, 1903.

On March 2, 1833, the President signed both bills—one yielding substantially what the Nullifiers had demanded and the other giving the President the requested authority to put down nullification—if there should be resistance when occasion for it had been removed. "Thus", in the words of Professor Sumner, "the olive branch and the rod were bound up together."

CHAPTER X

NULLIFICATION TRIUMPHANT? — CALHOUN'S PECU-
LIARITIES.—WHAT IT ALL MEANT.

The South Carolina convention reconvened
March 11, 1833, mainly to pass on this action of
Congress. Before the members of the State's
delegation in Washington had agreed to the compromise they perceived from the aid given the
"force bill" that nullification could be neither a
peaceable process nor enlist the help of any other
Southern State. Accordingly if they had not
accepted the compromise, as the masterful Hamilton said, they would have cut themselves off from
sympathy and had "the whole force of the em-
bodied public opinion of the South against us".[1]
The "force bill" had been passed and there had
been no halt in the collection of the customs duties,
but Hamilton's threat to submit the question of
secession to the State convention had not been carried out. And, except favorable opinion in South
Carolina, the attempt to establish nullification as a
principle of, or even a logical deduction from, the
Constitution was a total failure.

Yet politics naturally suggested calling nullification a success. By ignoring the significance of

[1] *S. C. Conv. of March, 1833*, p. 33.

168

the election of 1832 and the influence of the well-
known fact that the early payment of the national
debt would leave a large annual surplus to be
squandered unless the tariff of 1832 should be
greatly reduced, it was easy to believe that the
nullification convention had caused the revision.
McDuffie exclaimed: "I hereby solemnly declare,
in the presence of God, that the act of 1832 would
never have been touched, except for the acts of
this State." [2] And the March convention significantly pointed to the recent tariff law providing
for such a reduction of the duties as should ulti-
mately bring them to a revenue standard and not
exceed the needs of the Government when eco-
nomically administered. The truth seems to be
that various recent influences had doomed the
highly protective tariff [3] and that the nullification
movement had hastened its fall. The ordinance
of November 24, 1832, and the laws (except in
regard to the militia) to make it effective, were
soon repealed, by a vote of 153 to 4. [4]

Of course the "force bill", the "bloody act",
was like a thorn in the flesh. Because it emphat-

[2] *Ibid.*, 39.

[3] " The system would surely have been swept away within a
year or two if some of its adherents had not foreseen what was
to happen and taken security of the future."—1 Stanwood, 410.

[4] *Journals of Conventions* etc., 105, 110.

ically denied that South Carolina was sovereign, it was denounced as "calculated, when carried into practice, to destroy our constitutional frame of government, to subvert the public liberty and to bring about the utter ruin and abasement of the Southern States of this Confederacy", and was pronounced null and void in South Carolina.[5] McDuffie is said to have inquired how it was proposed to make null and void the military provisions of the bill, for he thought that something more than an ordinance would be required to nullify the army and the navy of the United States.[6]

The doctrine of state-sovereignty and of state-allegiance being mutually indispensable, the convention further declared and ordained that "the allegiance of the citizens of this State, while they continue such, is due to said State; and that obedience only, and not allegiance, is due by them to any other power or authority, to whom a control over them has been or may be delegated by the State".[7]

Viewed superficially, the contest was largely a draw. Perhaps this was well, for each side was partly right and partly wrong. Although most of South Carolina's doctrines about the Constitution

[5] *Ibid.*, 125, 132.
[6] Perry, 2 *Reminiscences*, 228.
[7] *Journals* etc., 132.

were both unsound and dangerous and her alleged sufferings on account of the tariff were exaggerated, her economic ideas were substantially correct and her grievances were ample to warrant indignant protests. These, being unavailing, had been impatiently transformed into unconstitutional resistance, which went to the verge of revolution, when it was most important that constitutional methods should be strictly adhered to. That was South Carolina's great offense. Common sense as clearly dictated the repeal of the protective tariff—without which nullification would not then have been attempted—as it did the adoption of the "force bill" against threatened revolution. It was indeed fortunate that there was no need of coercion on account of a thoroughly bad tariff law, and that a clear and positive declaration of nationalism, made by a large majority of Congress, answered the immediate purpose.

Although there had been no nullification in fact, but only in legal or, rather, illegal form, the repeal of the ordinance, after the tariff had been reduced, did not lessen the belief of the Nullifiers that they had been triumphant, as was shown by their promptly declaring the "force bill" null and void. Having forgotten their numerous threats to secede in case of an attempt to collect the duties by force, they heartily agreed with Turnbull in boasting that they had "tamed the pride of this arrogant Federal Government". "With our one-gun battery of Nullification, we have driven the enemy from his moorings, compelled him to slip his cable, and put to sea." [8] Nullification had at least manifested great vigor and gathered some of the emblems of success, while Nationalism had gone but little beyond asserting sound principles.

The leading Nullifiers were able, eloquent, energetic theorists, not constitutionalists, and had uncommon talents for agitation. They fancied themselves exponents of fundamental rights and sound principles of government, but they seemed to regard preaching revolution as the highest type of political activity. A great majority of the South was ready to coöperate with them in proper antagonism to the injustice of the protective tariff. By patient and sober discussion they could undoubtedly have won much support from the North and thereby have succeeded in a constitutional manner beneficial to the whole nation. But that seemed too commonplace. They believed that other Southern States would stand guard

[8] *Conv., March, 1833*, 35. Calhoun wrote, Mar. 24, 1833: " I have no doubt the [tariff] system has got its death wound. Nullification has dealt the fatal blow. We have applied the same remedy to the bloody act."—*Calhoun Corresp.*, 324.

while South Carolina dictated terms to the Federal Government. If the Government should yield, then South Carolina would win a glorious victory; if the Government should attempt coercion, then most of the Southern States would rush to South Carolina's aid. In either case South Carolina would be the leader and Calhoun the hero. With Jefferson's theories and prestige and Calhoun's magical reasoning on their side, they could not conceive of failure. They were neither statesmen nor patriots; they were impassioned "statriots" armed for high tragedy, but confident that all would end in melodrama. Petigru characterized them thus: "As citizens of the United States they are traitors, but as citizens of the State they are true men. In his immortal satire, 'Absolom *vs.* Achitophel', Dryden says of Sir William Jones, he

> ' could statutes draw
> To mean rebellions; make treason law.' " [9]

This was especially true of Calhoun, who in many respects was different from his fellow-leaders—more plausible, cautious and substantial but less oratorical and less audacious, except in theorizing, without being less ambitious and less self-confident. After he turned away from his early

[9] Carson, *Petigru*, 124.

and well-balanced nationalism, he became both an unbalanced theorist and an obsessed dogmatist, contending that nullification was "the fundamental principle of our system"—"in truth, the highest and most precious of all the rights of the States, and essential to preserve" the Union.[10]

What was most remarkable about his method was his marvelous skill in making artful generalizations and in glossing his sophistry with apparent frankness and an air of logic. His manner disarmed criticism, until after his false premises were well laid, and then it was almost impossible to escape his conclusions. Unless on guard, one was not likely to object to his referring to the Constitution as a compact between the States, or to the General Government as their agent in certain respects, or to his remarking that "the right of a State originally to complete self-government is a fundamental principle in our system". Starting with these and assuming (contrary to fact and the views of the authors of the Constitution) the indivisibilty of sovereignty, he very effectively argued that compacts are made between sovereign States, and when these create a government, that government is their agent and each State is necessarily and at all times a judge of the extent

[10] 6 *Works*, 168.

of the agency.[11] Because the Constitutional Convention rejected propositions to give the General Government excessive national powers, designed to reduce the States to something like the condition of mere Territories, and which therefore would probably have prevented the adoption of the Constitution, Calhoun insisted that no national powers were bestowed on the General Government, except as an agent.[12]

He must have known that the Confederation had been a wretched failure—weak, discordant, futile; that its government was by a single house of Congress, composed of delegates appointed annually and directly controlled and paid by their respective States; that each State had one vote, and that no law could be enacted without the approval of 9 of the 13 States, and that accordingly the mere inaction of any 5 prevented legislation; that the Congress lacked many prerequisites of a real government, and had no independent source of revenue, for each State for itself retained the right to levy taxes and to impose duties on imports and exports; that to pay the expenses of the common government the Congress must make a requisition on each State for its quota, which was paid or ignored at pleasure; that the Congress chose one

11 6 *Works*, 151-52.
12 6 *Works*, 154 ff.

of its members to act as president, who was only
a figurehead; and that during the recess of Congress a "Committee of the States", consisting of
one delegate from each, was the only ostensible
government, until necessity required the appointment of a head for each executive department.
Thus hampered, the Congress was given the control of the army, the navy, the diplomatic and the
postal service, with special limitations in regard
to some of them. Such were the chief features of
this government, which was a worse failure in
peace than in war.

It had become so great a source of weakness
and danger that the members of the Constitutional Convention of 1787, appointed exclusively
to revise the Articles of Confederation, decided
that the public welfare demanded the revolutionary act of throwing aside the whole machinery of
the Confederation and the creation of a very different and largely centralized government, supreme and virtually independent within its
sphere; with powers not only to pass laws by a
majority vote of the individual members of each
house but also to execute the laws; with a treasury
exclusively its own and the means of filling it;
with officers appointed by and solely responsible
to itself, and paid from its treasury, as should be
all members of the Congress; and this govern-

ment should be in many other respects self-sufficient, forceful and radically different from the Confederation. Yet in proportion as it should be strong and centralized concealment of the evidences of it was important, lest the fears of the small States and the prejudices of the less intelligent portion of the people should defeat efforts for reform. Even these 55 selected patriots of the Revolution were not able to work out a wholly logical and consistent form of government. But they persisted until they incorporated the best that they thought they could secure the ratification of by a special and sovereign convention in each State, instead of by the confederative Congress or the non-sovereign State legislatures.

That in the Constitution thus adopted the individual States did not retain their full sovereignty and that national powers with sovereignty in a wide field were bestowed on the General Government, these were amply shown by opinions of members of the Constitutional Convention; [13] by

13 Madison's letter of Apr. 8, 1787, to Edmund Randolph expressed the pre-convention purposes of the moderate nationalists, whose ideas were most nearly realized: " I hold it for a fundamental point, that an individual independence of the states is utterly irreconcilable with the idea of an aggregate sovereignty. I think at the same time, that a consolidation of the states into one simple republic is not less unattainable than it would be inexpedient. Let it be tried, then, whether any middle ground can be

the powers "granted" and "vested in" Congress,[14] "vested in one supreme Court";[15] by the all but unlimited power of amendment by Congress and three-fourths of the States;[16] and by the powers surrendered by and denied to the States,[17] and by making "this Constitution and

taken, which will at once support a due supremacy of the national authority, and leave in force the local authorities so far as they can be subordinately useful."—5 *Elliot's Debates*, 107.

The well-known covering letter that the members of the Constitutional Convention sent to Congress with the proposed Constitution said: "It is obviously impracticable, in the federal government of these states, to secure all rights of independent sovereignty to each, and yet provide for the interest and safety of all. Individuals entering into society must give up a share of liberty, to preserve the rest. The magnitude of the sacrifice must depend as well on situation and circumstances, as on the object to be obtained. It is at all times difficult to draw with precision the line between those rights which must be surrendered and those which may be reserved. And on the present occasion this difficulty was increased by a difference among the several states as to their situation, extent, habits, and particular interests.

"In all our deliberations on this subject, we kept steadily in our view that which appeared to us the greatest interest of every true American, the consolidation of our union, in which is involved our prosperity, felicity, safety, perhaps our national existence. This important consideration, seriously and deeply impressed on our minds, led each state in the Convention to be less rigid in points of inferior magnitude than might have been otherwise expected."—5 *Elliot's Debates*, 536.

[14] Article I, sections 1 and 8.

[15] Article III, sections 1 and 2.

[16] See *ante* p. 44.

[17] Article I, Section 10 reads: "No State shall enter into any Treaty, Alliance, or Confederation; grant Letters of Marque and Reprisal; coin Money; emit Bills of Credit; make any Thing

the Laws of the United States which shall be made in Pursuance thereof • • • the supreme Law of the Land; and [requiring that] the Judges in every State shall be bound thereby, any Thing in the Constitution or Laws of any State to the Contrary notwithstanding", and that "the Members of the several State Legislatures, and all executive and judicial Officers, both of the United States and of the several States, shall be bound by Oath or Affirmation, to support this Constitution".[18] These and other evidences of nationality nearly enabled the opponents of the Constitution to defeat it in the State conventions, by alleging that it would destroy the States and make a consolidated government. Nevertheless Calhoun stoutly asserted: "But however dissimilar their governments, the

but gold and silver Coin a Tender in Payment of Debts; pass any Bill of Attainder, ex post facto Law, or Law impairing the Obligation of Contracts, or grant any Title of Nobility.

No State shall, without the Consent of the Congress, lay any Imposts or Duties on Imports or Exports, except what may be absolutely necessary for executing it's inspection Laws: and the net Produce of all Duties and Imposts, laid by any State on Imports or Exports, shall be for the Use of the Treasury of the United States; and all such Laws shall be subject to the Revision and Controul of the Congress.

No State shall, without the Consent of Congress, lay any Duty of Tonnage, keep Troops, or Ships of War in time of Peace, enter into any Agreement or Compact with another State, or with a foreign Power, or engage in War, unless actually invaded, or in such imminent Danger as will not admit of delay."

[18] Art. VI.

present *Constitution is as far removed from consolidation, and is strictly and as purely a confederation, as the one which it superseded."* "The new Government was reared on the foundation of the old, strengthened, but not changed".[19] And reasoning by the unanalogous law of agency of course it was not difficult to convince the uninformed and the credulous.[20]

Thus he undertook to create, outside of the Constitution, an imaginary super-constitution that should justify nullification, make it a peaceable process, adequate to the needs of a small minority for defense against a large majority. And the purpose of the theory that the citizens of a State owed allegiance solely to their State was to enable each State to control the entire physical power of its citizens and thereby leave the General Government helpless,—in Madison's simile, like an empty scabbard in the hand of a soldier. Lest nullification might not suffice in all cases, Calhoun had ready a theory of secession designed to enable a State to renounce its ties to the Union and to depart in peace.[21]

This was the man that in 1816 had warned his countrymen of "a new and terrible danger, Dis-

[19] 6 *Works*, 158, 185.
[20] 6 *Works*, 168-69.
[21] 6 *Works*, 168-69.

union", against which "we ought to be perpetually guarded".

Following Dr. Cooper's suggestion, South Carolina had "calculated the value of the Union", but was undecided whether to represent it by an interrogation point or a minus sign. Hayne's report to the November, 1832, convention expressed grave doubt "whether it be in the nature of things possible, to hold together such a Confederacy as ours, by any means short of military despotism, after it has degenerated into a CONSOLIDATED GOVERNMENT". In the March convention Robert Barnwell Smith (Rhett) challenged members to lay their hands on their hearts and say, that they were ardently attached to the Union of these States. "Why, have we not for the last seven years, been declaiming against this Union, as inflicting upon us oppression and poverty and desolation? * * * Sir, if a Confederacy of the Southern States could now be obtained, should we not deem it a happy termination—happy beyond expectation, of our long struggle for our rights against oppression?" [22] More than a few others would have welcomed disunion at once. [23] A large minority, while still deprecating

---

[22] *Conv. of Mar., 1833*, 24, 25.

[23] P. Phillips, a Unionist from Chesterfield district, said: " Sir,

it, because of the hazards, expected that some day changed conditions would bring about a Southern Confederacy and wonderful prosperity. Even eight months before the nullification convention Chancellor Harper had publicly expressed this solemn opinion: "Let the Southern States once taste the advantage, so far as wealth is concerned, of a separate existence, and they are not likely to seek the Union again." [24]

There was an obvious conflict of interests between freedom and slavery. McDuffie believed that "a still more imperious necessity of resistance" lay beneath the present question: it was the rivalry between the free labor of the North and the slave labor of the South.[25] Judge Harper thought that the trend of consolidation might next be "to relieve another 'disfranchised class', whom your laws are alleged to oppress—your free

among my own neighbors there are men whom I know to possess honest motives, openly declaring that they can join neither of the present parties—but wait the formation of one which shall go boldly and openly for Disunion."—*Conv. of Mar., 1833,* 66.

[24] Speech in Charleston, Apr. 1, 1832, p. 10.

Petigru wrote Apr. 15, 1833: "I believe they intend to open for a Southern Confederacy soon."—Carson, 122. And July 15, 1833: "But nullification has done its work; it has prepared the minds of men for a separation of the States, and when the question is mooted again it will be distinctly union or disunion."—Carson, 125.

[25] *Conv. March, 1833,* 41.

negroes, first; and afterwards, your slaves".[26] "A people, owning slaves, are mad, or worse than mad, who do not hold their destinies in their own hands," cried Robert Barnwell Smith. "Do we not bear the insolent assumption by our rulers, that slave labor shall not come into competition with free? Nor is it our Northern brethren alone—the whole world are in arms against your institutions. Every stride of this Government, over your rights, brings it nearer and nearer to your peculiar policy * * *. South Carolina must be an armed camp. She has no rights under this Government, but what she is prepared to assert in the tented field." [27]

Political ambition clouded Calhoun's vision and often made him secretive and politic in action. He habitually avowed love for the Union, as every aspirant for the Presidency of the whole country must do. The Union he loved was not that of the Constitution, but the fanciful confederative agency that he believed his dogmas could make a reality.[28]

[26] *Ibid.*, 50.

[27] *Ibid.*, 25, 27.

[28] "I feel assured, that it [the Fort Hill 'Address' of July 26, 1831] contains the only principles by which our constitution, our Union and liberty can be preserved."—*Corresp.*, 297. The "Address" declared his love for the Union, but showed that a prerequisite of that love was a Union based on what he considered the "only solid foundation".—6 *Works*, 61. He fondly

This longed-for agency-Union he cherished and was sentimental about; and it meant nothing to the contrary that, with his natural caution, great experience in public affairs and his still ardent ambition for the Presidency, he dreaded secession by a single State—all that was then possible. Yet to Turnbull, Hamilton, McDuffie, Dr. Cooper, Robert Barnwell Smith and other leaders, who had the courage of their convictions and had despaired of the Union, the actual Federal Government, with its national powers in operation and approved by Congress, was not more hateful than it was to Calhoun, who viewed it as a monster with a hundred arms.[29]

Near the conclusion of the nullification struggle, Robert Barnwell Smith gravely remarked: "Let gentlemen not be deceived. It is not the Tariff—not Internal Improvements—nor yet the Force Bill, which constitutes the great evil against

looked back to the resolutions of 1798 and 1799, which he called "the principles that brought the Republican party into power in 1801."—*Corresp.*, 296. "We must return to the Whig [Republican] doctrines of '98. Nothing but a thorough reform can save us—and that cannot be long delayed, without utter ruin."—*Corresp.*, 317.

[29] " And he thought it [disunion] best [if " matters continued going forward "], for the system of plunder [by means of the tariff] such as it was now [,] was the most despicable of all possible forms of Government."—J. H. Hammond's interview with Calhoun, March, 18, 1831, 6 *Amer. Hist. Rev.*, 744.

which we are contending. These are but the symptoms of the disease—but not the disease itself. * * * but it is the despotism which constitutes the evil: and until this Government is made a limited Government, and is confined to those interests which are common to the whole Confederacy, there is no liberty—no security for the South.'' [30] Therefore the Constitution must be changed, for the leaders of the nullification movement considered that they had only temporarily dealt with one of the minor dangers supposed to be impending. And unless the Constitution could be interpreted so as to agree with Calhoun's dogmas and to disagree with the nationalism of which Webster's replies to Hayne and Calhoun, Jackson's proclamation and the ''force bill'' were popular expressions, South Carolina was at the beginning rather than near the end of a revolutionary struggle.

The March convention, expecting a still greater struggle, approved a report saying: ''Let this contest be carried on firmly, steadily, without passion and without faltering''.[31] Turnbull urged: ''Let us follow up our recent victory by preparing in time for the new conflict, which sooner or later must come''.[32] And Judge Harper insisted:

[30] *Conv. of March, 1833*, 26.
[31] *Journals of Conventions, 1832, 1833, 1852,* p. 131.
[32] *Conv. of March, 1833*, p. 62.

"Finally, we must regard ourselves as at the beginning, not at the end, of a contest. In less than another year, we may be called to arms".[33] Leadership and public sentiment in the State were in an almost perfect condition to agitate for such a struggle. Because it was foreseen that this struggle would be violent, McDuffie warned the March convention and the public that "all our peculiar circumstances—all our institutions—render a thorough system of defence absolutely indispensable to our safety, as well as freedom. Our militia should be as well trained as the armies of Napoleon." [34] In fact, to the leaders and many thousand other persons nationalism had become hateful, state sovereignty had become vainglorious and a Southern Confederacy was a fond dream. South Carolina had indeed cut loose from her past. Even the traditions of nationalism had nearly vanished. The Nullifiers, with Calhoun at their head, were determined to pursue their notions of the interests of South Carolian and hoped to induce the rest of the lower South to follow their leadership in opposition to nationalism and a rapidly increasing majority, which would inevitably, in a few decades, at most, become antislavery.

[33] *Ibid.*, 52.
[34] *Ibid.*, 41

INDEX

A

ADAMS, JOHN QUINCY, 30, 64n
ALABAMA
    legislature on protection, 18
ALIEN AND THE SEDITION ACTS, 77

B

BENTON, THOMAS H., 62, 65
    on tariff of 1816, 5–6
    on tariff of 1828, 10–11
    attacked the Foot resolution, 56
    on Webster, 63
    said Webster spoke *at* Calhoun in debate with Hayne, 161
BLAIR, GENERAL JAMES, 99
BOUCHER, CHAUNCEY SAMUEL, 26n, 95n
BRECKINRIDGE, JOHN, 78
BURGESS, PROFESSOR J. W., 150n

C

CALHOUN, JOHN C.
    on tariff bill of 1816, 2–5
    his casting vote defeated woollens bill of 1827, 10
    on the effect of the tariff, 23n
    not responsible for tariff of 1824 or of 1828, 34
    aspirant for the Presidency, 34 ff., 35n, 102 ff., 106, 108
    his non-committalism, 35 ff., 102
    on the great defect in our system, 35
    must show South Carolinians that he was not a protectionist, 36
    hastened home in May, 1828, 36
    on excitement about the tariff, 36
    consulted by many politicians, 37
    his autobiography, 37
    could see but two possible remedies, 38
    on "State Interposition or the Veto", 38

187